Thick-Film Hybrids

Manufacture and Design

Malcolm R. Haskard

Microelectronics Centre
South Australian Institute of Technology and
Technical Manager
Australian Silicon Technology, Adelaide

PRENTICE HALL

New York London Toronto Sydney Tokyo

Prentice Hall, Inc., *Englwood Cliffs, New Jersey*
Prentice Hall of Australia, *Sydney*
Prentice Hall Canada, Inc., *Toronto*
Prentice Hall Hispanoamerica, SA, *Mexico*
Prentice Hall of India Private Ltd, *New Delhi*
Prentice Hall International, Inc., *London*
Prentice Hall of Japan, Inc., *Tokyo*
Prentice Hall of Southeast Asia Pty Ltd, *Singapore*
Editoria Prentice Hall do Brasil Ltda, *Rio de Janeiro*

Typeset by Monoset Typesetters, Strathpine, Queensland.

Printed and bound in Australia by
Impact Printing, Brunswick, Victoria.

Cover design by Kim Webber.
Cover photograph courtesy of Plessey Australia.

1 2 3 4 5 92 91 90 89 88
ISBN 0 7248 1194 X
US ISBN 0-13-917113-4

National Library of Australia
Cataloguing-in-Publication Data

Haskard, M.R. (Malcolm Rosswyn).
  Thick film hybrids.

  Includes index.
  ISBN 0 7248 1194 X

  1. Thick films. 2. Microelectronics.
  I. Title.

621.381'7

Library of Congress
Cataloguing-in-Publication Data

Haskard, M.R. (Malcolm R.), 1936–
  Thick film hybrids/Malcolm R. Haskard.

    p/   cm.
  Bibliography: p.
  ISBN 0-13-917113-4
  1 Thick-film circuits. I. Title
TK7871.15.F5H36 1988
621.381'7—dc19   87–32907
                                          CIP

PRENTICE HALL

A division of Simon & Schuster

K E G Pitt BSc, CChem,, FRSC, MInstP
Principal Lecturer
Microelectronics Centre
Middlesex Polytechnic
Bounds Green Road, N11 2NQ

Keith Pitt
5 Pipers Close
Hove BN3 8FG
East Sussex
Tel (01273) 424459

Thick-Film Hybrids

Manufacture and Design

To my father:

Scientist, teacher, gentleman, Christian

Contents

Foreword   ix

Preface   xi

Chapter 1   **Introduction to thick-film technology**   **1**
                     1.1 History   1
                     1.2 An overview of the thick-film process   3
                     1.3 Comparison with other technologies   8
                     1.4 Exercises   11
                     1.5 References   14

Chapter 2   **Screens and printing**   **15**
                     2.1 Printing   15
                     2.2 Screens   16
                     2.3 Squeegee   22
                     2.4 The substrate holder   27
                     2.5 Operation and frame   27
                     2.6 Film thickness measurement   28
                     2.7 Thick-film writing machines   28
                     2.8 Exercises   28
                     2.9 References   29

Chapter 3   **Paste and substrate material systems**   **31**
                     3.1 Introduction   31
                     3.2 Noble metal based paste systems   32
                     3.3 Base-metal pastes and substrates   40
                     3.4 Paste and system selection   41
                     3.5 Exercises   43
                     3.6 References   44

Chapter 4   **The firing and trimming processes**   **45**
                     4.1 The remaining screen processing steps   45
                     4.2 Firing of pastes   45
                     4.3 Component trimming   49
                     4.4 Exercises   55
                     4.5 References   55

Chapter 5   **Assembly, packaging and testing**   **57**
5.1 The final steps   57
5.2 Chip assembly   57
5.3 Packaging   67
5.4 Testing   68
5.5 References   69

Chapter 6   **Cleanliness and safety**   **70**
6.1 Introduction   70
6.2 Clean rooms   70
6.3 Quality materials   75
6.4 Safety   75
6.5 References   76

Chapter 7   **Basic design concepts**   **78**
7.1 Process limitations   78
7.2 Component types   78
7.3 Printed width and spacing   80
7.4 Scaling components and aspect ratios   82
7.5 Quality of a component   83
7.6 Typical layout rules   87
7.7 Computer aided design (CAD)   90
7.8 Exercises   96
7.9 References   96

Chapter 8   **Additional circuit design concepts**   **98**
8.1 Introduction   98
8.2 Low-frequency circuit design   98
8.3 Multi-layer circuits   102
8.4 High-frequency circuits   104
8.5 Thick film at microwave frequencies   106
8.6 Thermal considerations   113
8.7 Exercises   116
8.8 References   117

Chapter 9   **Thick-film sensors**   **120**
9.1 Introduction   120
9.2 Sensors based on special pastes   123
9.3 Sensors based on standard pastes   123
9.4 Other related devices   130
9.5 Exercises   131
9.6 References   131

Appendix A   **Screen care and preparation   135**
A.1 Screen pre-preparation   135
A.2 Polyblue mask preparation   135
A.3 Screen preparation   137
A.4 Cleaning screens after printing   137

Appendix B   **Summary of thick-film layout rules   139**

Appendix C   **Etchant solutions for pastes   142**
C.1 Gold pastes   142
C.2 Gold-palladium pastes   142
C.3 Silver pastes   142
C.4 Silver-palladium pastes   142
C.5 Copper pastes   143

Index   145

Foreword

Thick-film technology first appeared in the early 1960s as a relatively crude and cheap approach for the manufacture of resistor/conductor networks for mass production applications. Since then it has grown spectacularly both in areas of application and in the quality of the product. It has not yet stopped developing in the late 1980s under the pressure of VLSI development. However, far from being squeezed out by silicon on the one hand and surface-mounted technology for printed circuit boards on the other, it is finding new and more critical applications.

Many books have been written on the technology at advanced levels but the learner, whether at college or in industry, has mainly been neglected. Colleges and universities have thick-film facilities for research and project applications but the undergraduate and postgraduate student is forced to wade through much data which is irrelevant and often incomprehensible to the beginner. There is a need for an introduction to the technology we shall be using in the 1990s for newcomers both to industry and to the various areas within industry.

This book is an attempt to deal with the problem. The author has combined his experience in electronics teaching and thick-film technology to put forward a wide-ranging introductory text. It is the direct result of many years experience in the School of Electronic Engineering of the South Australian Institute of Technology in the teaching of courses in hybrid technology.

Different readers will have different expectations from this book. The nine chapters and three appendices have been designed to cover as broad a front in thick-film technology as possible. They are backed up by references for each chapter for further investigation. One unusual feature for the subject is the provision of copious exercises so that the students can check their comprehension of what they have read. The subject of screens and printing is very rarely covered in adequate detail for the newcomer but here a detailed chapter is devoted to it with numerous illustrations. This is one area where students find it difficult to visualize the artefacts and processes. This treatment should minimize the problem.

In addition to traditional thick-film subjects like materials and processes, assembly of semiconductor devices is also covered in the hybrid context. The newcomer will very much appreciate the detailed sections on design and applications.

Two unique chapters for a book on thick-film hybrid technology make a special contribution. It is not easy to find an up-to-date treatment of both safety and environmental control in this field. This chapter will make the relevance of industrial precautions extremely clear. The author's own special expertise in sensor technology is presented in a chapter of its own which discusses a broad range of aspects of hybrid sensors and their materials, processes and applications.

Although this book is described as an introduction, it is more than that. It is a presentation of many of the more important aspects of current industrial technology. As such it will find use both in academic circles and also in industry, for example, for training purposes or for a readable resumé of a broad technology.

The demise of thick-film technology has long been forecast. However, it is still flourishing and developing both in its own right and as a support for integrated circuits. The author has given the field a very strong vote of confidence by going straight to the people who either need to know or will be at that stage in the future. In 25 years thick-film technology has gone a very long way from screen-printed slab resistors on alumina-trimmed by sandblasting. This book heralds the next 25 years and has been written to help those people who will one day become responsible for its future to make a start in the subject.

Keith Pitt
Middlesex Polytechnic Microelectronics Centre
Bounds Green, London, U.K.

February 1988

Preface

Having been involved in thick-film hybrid technology for 17 years and having taught the subject for the past seven, I am aware that there is a real need for an up-to-date textbook on the subject, one which covers many of the new products and ideas. The majority of books on thick-film microelectronics were written at least a decade ago and cover only the high temperature noble metal/metal oxide pastes and associated circuit manufacture. The low temperature polymer pastes, for example, are already having a tremendous impact on consumer products and, in the years ahead, will move into other areas.

Most books books on the subject do not give a complete overview of the field. For example, sensors, today a topic of importance, are never discussed. Few books touch on the topics of microstrip and RF thick film. In this volume, I have endeavored to cover all important topics so that the reader can obtain an understanding of the full potential of thick-film hybrid technology including design, manufacture, and applications.

I am most grateful for the constructive comments made on the original draft by my friends Keith Pitt of Middlesex Polytechnic, London, and Dr Nihal Sinnadurai of the European Chapter of the International Society of Hybrid Microelectronics.

A special thanks must be given to my able colleague, John Bannigan, who over the years has assisted me by managing and operating our production and testing facilities.

Malcolm R. Haskard
Microelectronics Centre
South Australian Institute of Technology

Acknowledgments

The photographs throughout this book are used with the kind permissions from Philips Australia, Plessey Australia, and Microelectronics Centre, South Australia.

1 Introduction to thick-film technology

1.1   History

At present, the world is going through its second industrial revolution—the microelectronic explosion. While people tend to concentrate on the silicon chip, this is only one aspect of the revolution. Microelectronics consists of several important technologies which can be classified as shown in Figure 1.1. The power of the technology is not simply in the complexity that can be accommodated in a given volume, but also the diversity of what can be achieved, for example, the frequency and power range, security of design and size of economic production runs. Figure 1.2 shows several of these microelectronic technologies. An important element in all of this is the thick-film process, particularly when it is combined with integrated circuits to form hybrid components. It is a very cost-competitive manufacturing technology, allowing small or large volume automated production runs producing units with such robustness that they can be employed in cars or missiles.

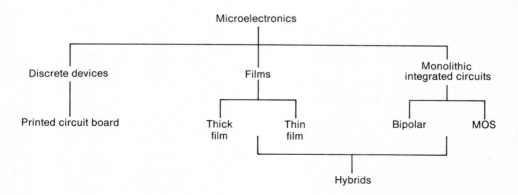

Figure 1.1   Microelectronic technique classifications

Surprisingly, it was through the 'missile program' developed during World War II that thick-film technology came about. It is therefore the oldest of all the microelectronic technologies developed to produce a product in volume (Cadenhed and DeCoursey, 1985). Using silver-based inks or pastes and primitive silk-screening methods, electronic proximity fuses for bombs were made. Although the thick-film industry had its foundations in the 1940s, it was not until the 1960s that the technology was used in any real way in commercial products. IBM, in conjunction with Du Pont, developed a series of pastes based on palladium known as the 7800 series. These pastes were used by IBM in its 360 computer series (Davis et al., 1964). Today the types and range of pastes are many and the versatility and applications of the thick-film technique are growing continually. Figure 1.3 illustrates several thick-film products.

Figure 1.2   Selection of various microelectronic technology products
Source: With permission from Philips Australia.

Over the years, the silk-screening process had not been the only method used to produce a film circuit. Vacuum deposition, electroplating, spin on and etching, painting or spraying and dye stamping are examples of alternative processes. Some are still employed today. Vacuum deposition, with or without thickening by electroplating, is today an alternative film process and is called 'thin film'. The names 'thick' and 'thin' suggest that the difference between the two technologies is the thickness of the material laid down. Such is not the case. By and large, a thin-film circuit refers to a circuit deposited by a vacuum deposition (evaporation, sputtering, etc.) process, whereas a thick-film circuit means a screening process has been employed.

The thick-film process will now be considered in more detail and then compared to the alternative technologies.

Figure 1.3   Assortment of thick-film products
Source: With permission from Philips Australia.

1.2   An overview of the thick-film process

The process consists of a number of simple steps which are repeated several times in the correct sequence. These steps are screen manufacture, printing and firing. To these a number of standard electronic processes must be added including cleaning, soldering, electrical test and packaging.

The basic step to the process is the screening. It is the same process that has been used by the printing and fabric-making industries for generations. The inks, or pastes here, are pushed through a screen by a squeegee, made of a pliable material. Only where there are holes in the screen will the paste come through. Thus the pattern on the screen defines the resultant pattern printed on the substrate. Since an electrical circuit is to be printed, the substrate must be an insulator such as alumina, polyester or porcelain-coated steel.

Let us consider the manufacture of the simple transistor circuit given in Figure 1.4. Because the transistor cannot be screen-printed, it must be added as a discrete surface-mounted component or silicon die, later to be wire bonded out.

Before production can occur, the circuit must be produced as a two-dimensional layout which defines where conductor tracks run, the size, shape and position of resistors and capacitors, allowing space for pads of appropriate size for external connections and the mounting of chip components including semi-

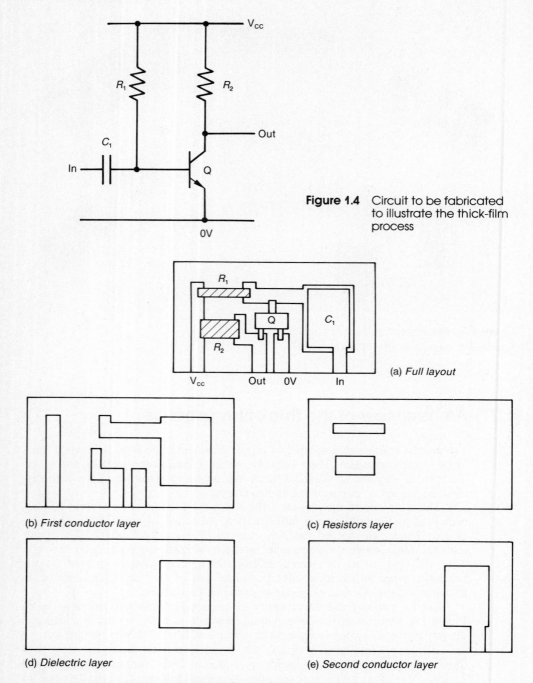

Figure 1.4 Circuit to be fabricated to illustrate the thick-film process

(a) *Full layout*

(b) *First conductor layer*

(c) *Resistors layer*

(d) *Dielectric layer*

(e) *Second conductor layer*

Figure 1.5 Layout of the simple transistor amplifier

conductor devices (Figure 1.5(a)). The layout consists of several layers, a layer being required for each different paste type. Thus there will be a lower conductor paste layer, resistor paste layer, insulator paste layer and second upper conductor paste layer. Such a circuit would require four screens, one for each layer (Figure 1.5).

The physical size of the resistors is calculated from the property of paste to be used, called 'sheet resistance'. This term allows the transformation of a three-dimensional process into one that is two-dimensional or planar. The assumption is that the screen-printing process will always print a constant thickness.

Thus a resistor of dimensions shown in Figure 1.6 has a resistance R given by:

$$R = \rho \frac{L}{t\,W}$$

$$= R_s \frac{L}{W} \tag{1.1}$$

where:

$$R_s = \frac{\rho}{t}$$

ρ is the bulk resistivity of the paste material
t is the constant thickness

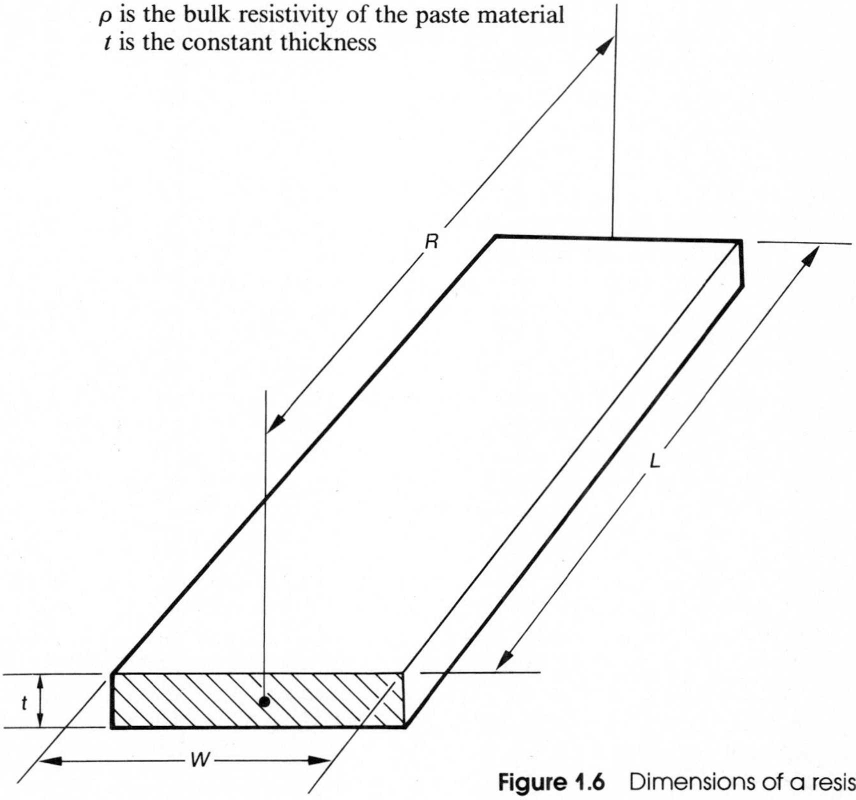

Figure 1.6 Dimensions of a resistor

R_s is called the sheet resistance of the paste. To determine the size of an L and W for a given resistor (say R_1), if R_1 is greater than R_s we need a long resistor so W will be the smaller dimension. By making W the minimum dimension the process allows (assuming other factors like dissipation do not cause a problem), we can now design a resistor of the correct value of minimum possible dimensions. That is, knowing R_1, R_s and W, we can calculate L from equation 1.1. Should R_1 be less than R_s then L will be the smaller dimension, to be made the minimum value set by the process and W can then be calculated.

For the capacitor, if the printed thickness of the dielectric is constant, then a given dielectric paste has a fixed capacitance per unit area. For a known capacity value requirement C_1, the area can now be computed. We will see later that a chip capacitor is often preferred to a printed one. However, in this example we will print one to illustrate the process more fully.

Returning to the resultant artwork for each of the four layers, they are next transferred to a mesh screen by a photographic process. The mesh of plastic or stainless steel is tightly stretched over a frame. Using a light-sensitive, thick emulsion coating on the screen, and exposing the screen through actual size positives of the artwork to ultraviolet light, the portions of the emulsion where printing is not to occur are polymerized by the light and do not dissolve away during the development stage. The resulting screens, one for each layer, will define the areas to be printed, for they are covered with emulsion (preventing any paste from being squeezed through except for the small section defined by the original artwork) and photographically removed.

In order to produce the circuit of Figure 1.4, the thick-film process would proceed as follows:

1. The four screens must be made.
2. The first conductor is printed, allowed to settle and dry, and then fired so that it can be transformed to its final composition.
3. The dielectric is printed, dried and fired. The dielectric is processed before the resistors, as the firing temperature is often higher. Two printings of dielectric may be undertaken to ensure there are no pin holes to cause a short circuit.
4. The upper conductor is printed, dried, but not necessarily fired.
5. Each firing may cause a change in the sheet resistance so that it is good policy to fire resistors as late as possible in a process. The resistors are printed, dried and cofired with the conductor. Should the pastes not allow cofiring, separate firings must be employed. Similarly, separate firings may occur after the printing of each of the two dielectric layers.

While this completes the printing process, various other steps are required to complete the products. If the ± 20 percent printing tolerance of the resistors is not sufficient, resistors can be trimmed (up only) in value by removing some of the paste, using a laser or an air abrader. Next, the small outline package transistor must be surface-mounted by soldering it in place. The circuit can then be tested and, if it performs satisfactorily, can be packaged or encapsulated in a dip plastic. A final inspection, test and product branding completes the manufacturing process.

Figure 1.7 is a flow diagram of a more general thick-film process allowing several options, while Figure 1.8 is the circuit diagram and layout of a thick-film product.

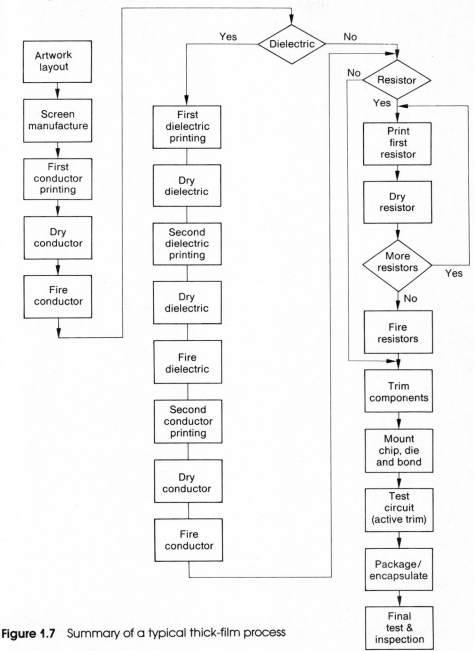

Figure 1.7   Summary of a typical thick-film process

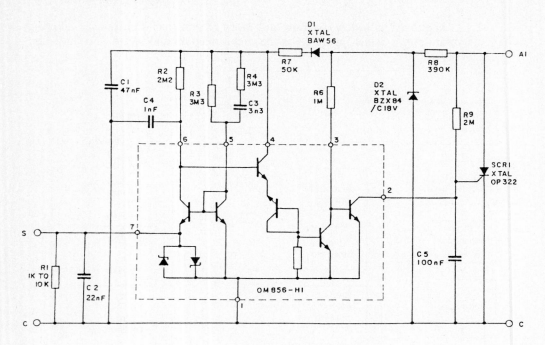

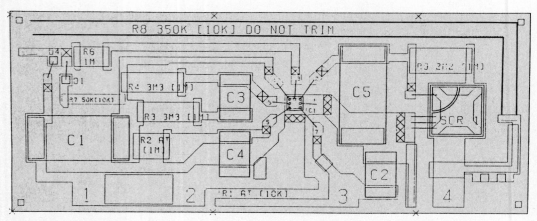

Figure 1.8   Circuit diagram and thick-film layout design for a commercially available product

Source: With permission from Philips Australia.

1.3   Comparison with other technologies

As illustrated in Figure 1.1, there are a number of microelectronic technologies in use today. Why is thick film the preferred method for so many products? Before answering this question, a brief statement on each of the other processes should be given.

The printed circuit or wiring board was developed after World War II and quickly became the industry standard for mass production, as it allowed repeatable characteristics. Originally, single-sided copper board was used, but with the passage of time more complex systems became possible, including flexible and multilayer types, with double-sided, plated-through hole, currently being the most common type. There is, however, a growing shift to using surface-mount techniques, in an attempt to reduce both size and costs and to accommodate VLSI packages with large pin counts. The laminate used for the board comes in various thicknesses and grades with fiberglass types of 1.6 mm thickness being common. Copper thickness is often expressed by weight such as 1 oz (35 microns thick) or $\frac{1}{2}$ oz (17.5 microns).

Surface-mounting techniques are the normal method of mounting chip components (such as resistors, capacitors, packaged transistors and integrated circuits) to thick-film substrates. No holes are required in the substrate as components are reflow soldered to the tracks on the surface of the substrate. The reason for this is that most substrates used in thick-film manufacture are alumina. The cost of ultrasonically or laser drilling holes for leaded components is high. Further, the holes weaken the substrates. The move by printed wiring manufacturers to use surface-mounted techniques has much to commend it, but there are many difficulties that need to be overcome before it can become a mature process.

Thin film, as already discussed, normally involves vacuum deposition technology. It can offer an order improvement in performance and is superior for microstrip work. However, the costs of materials and plant are considerably higher than those required for thick film.

Monolithic integrated circuit manufacture employs the most sophisticated of technologies. From the invention of the transistor by Shockley and his team in 1948, it took only ten years for the development of the integrated circuit. Since that day, their complexity in terms of the number of transistors on a chip has been doubling every year. At present, over a million transistors can be made in a single silicon chip. The processes used to do this include:

- oxidization;
- ion implantation of impurities;
- chemical vapor deposition of polysilicon;
- vacuum deposition of metals; and
- plasma etching.

While integrated circuits provide the highest component packing densities, they have limitations, and where the ultimate in performance is required, be it power, frequency response or resolution, they must be combined with one of the other microelectronic technologies to form a hybrid circuit. The marrying of the thick-film process, suitable for passive components, and integrated circuits, whose dominant component is the active transistor, brings about electronic systems that are of low cost and high performance.

In summary, thick film is complementary to integrated circuit technology. It competes directly with thin film, but has a considerable cost advantage. With printed circuit board, thick film offers at least a 4 to 1 size reduction over the conventional double-sided plated-through hole process. Where surface-mounted techniques are used on printed wiring boards, the size reduction advantage is reduced. However, other advantages (such as printing of resistors, mature process and thermal compatibility between substrate material and VLSI ceramic integrated packages) still make thick film an important process. Thus, where inexpensive and

Parameter	Printed circuit board	Thick film	Thin film	Monolithic bipolar and MOS
Capital cost production line	Lowest	Low	Medium	High
Quantity economic break point small plant	10	10	10	1000
Relative cost such units	Low	Low	Medium–High	Medium–High
Components on process	Conductor Small inductors	Conductors Resistors Small capacitors Small inductors	Conductors Resistors Small capacitors Small inductors	Conductors Small capacitors and resistors Diodes Transistors
Typical absolute tolerance components	—	± 20%	± 10%	− 50% to 100%
Trim component	—	Yes	Yes	Yes (some using zener zaping, etc.)
Matching component	—	± 1%	± 0.5%	± 2%
Typical physical size	Largest	Medium	Medium	Small
Typical time to design and manufacture full custom product	Low	Low	Low–Medium	Medium–High
RF and microwave applications	Yes strip line	Yes micro strip	Yes micro strip	Yes (GaAs)

Table 1.1 Comparison of same properties of the various manufacturing technologies

robust circuits are required, be they for consumer, professional or military products, thick film has much to offer.

Finally, thick film is conceptually a simple process which can be semi or fully automated. Consequently, the range of production facilities that can be established starts from inexpensive semimanual right through to a fully automatic factory requiring little human intervention. Table 1.1 compares the various technologies.

1.4   Exercises

1. Assuming a sheet resistance of 1000 ohm per square and a minimum dimension of 0.5 mm, calculate the dimensions of the smallest rectangular resistor to give a resistance of:
    (a) 250 ohm;
    (b) 1 kohm;
    (c) 2000 ohm.

2. A particular dielectric gives a capacitance of 0.5 pF/mm². A double printing of the dielectric is used to ensure there will be no pin hole shorts. Calculate the area required to give a capacitance of 100 pF. State any assumption made.

3. Figure 1.9 gives the layout of a pie and a 'T' attenuator pad and a 600 ohm load, while Table 1.2 gives measured values for 50 units as printed. Figure 1.10 shows a completed unit. Plot a histogram for R_1. Calculate the average value of resistance, range and percentage tolerance for all seven resistors. Assuming that the resistor dimensions as designed are correct, examine the effects of:
    (a) printing tolerance;
    (b) printing direction of the squeegee;
    (c) resistor position on the substrate;
    (d) matching between equal value resistors.
    Is the process stable?
    Are the attenuator pads acceptable for marketing?
    Why are the majority of the resistors less than the design value?

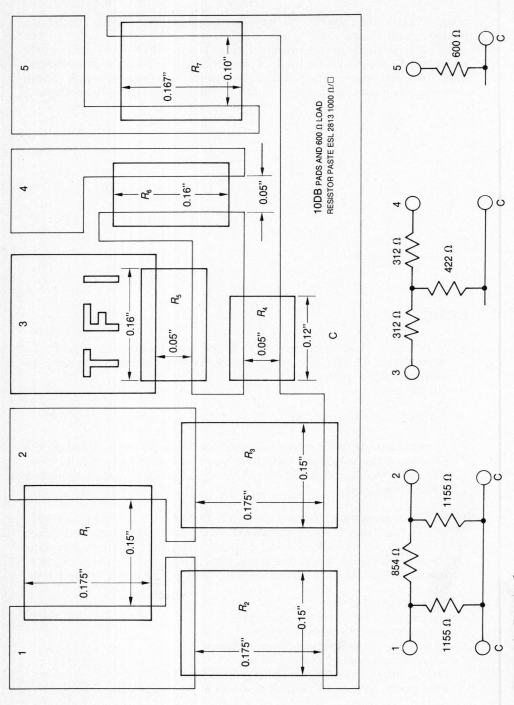

Figure 1.9 Exercise 3

Substrate number	Resistor on substrate						
	1	*2*	*3*	*4*	*5*	*6*	*7*
1	840	1120	1122	403	298	300	587
2	806	985	1051	388	298	286	540
3	821	1105	1096	397	306	296	572
4	870	1160	1168	416	319	314	596
5	854	1170	1141	438	332	311	597
6	751	1033	994	382	270	285	544
7	757	1050	1028	430	276	302	529
8	804	1074	1065	406	279	294	544
9	764	1058	1045	386	289	426	525
10	837	1270	1205	460	429	286	692
11	767	1041	1031	397	289	303	550
12	765	1080	1039	391	274	293	552
13	762	1048	1041	381	270	285	519
14	807	1118	1053	400	275	323	571
15	752	1057	1049	393	288	286	529
16	780	1059	1044	384	271	298	559
17	788	1060	1048	373	271	287	547
18	478	571	637	279	180	164	309
19	802	1000	1064	374	273	286	508
20	769	1069	1046	383	269	282	553
21	776	1059	1059	383	286	290	544
22	774	1054	1011	386	278	301	544
23	803	1109	1092	394	286	312	552
24	756	1059	1036	385	267	279	513
25	780	1086	1058	381	279	303	531
26	813	1102	1084	407	289	314	577
27	810	1116	1094	416	287	310	562
28	831	1077	1077	425	314	343	588
29	851	1116	1117	422	315	348	580
30	843	1102	1102	420	312	331	592
31	756	1053	989	366	278	292	530
32	836	1130	1117	419	314	337	591
33	847	1145	1094	422	319	336	601
34	794	1071	1041	417	298	309	557
35	793	1092	1092	427	325	331	580
36	700	911	944	371	271	287	498
37	784	977	979	354	275	309	550
38	597	891	1012	349	279	283	558
39	806	1107	1082	414	309	318	546
40	775	1022	1065	371	299	303	539
41	764	1038	1024	385	259	275	530
42	732	1019	989	366	268	274	514
43	810	1088	1055	413	301	330	602

(Continued overleaf)

Substrate number	Resistor on substrate						
	1	*2*	*3*	*4*	*5*	*6*	*7*
44	836	1100	1091	415	303	336	601
45	762	1000	1052	412	288	303	541
46	780	1079	1028	400	289	303	561
47	772	1068	1034	408	303	319	562
48	798	1057	1032	405	291	324	575
49	729	895	956	374	265	281	557
50	782	1201	1060	407	300	313	563
Average value							
Range							
% Tolerance							
Design value	854	1155	1155	422	312	312	600

Table 1.2 Measured values for 50 units as printed

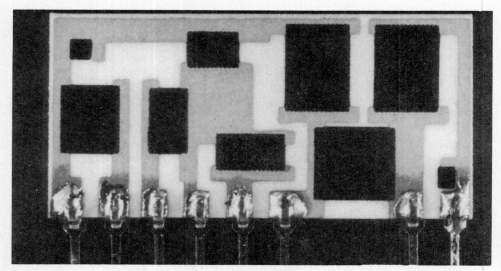

Figure 1.10 Completed pie and "T" alternator pad
Source: With permission from Microelectronics Centre, Australian Institute of Technology.

1.5 References

Cadenhed, R. L. and D. T. DeCoursey (1985), 'The History of Microelectronics Part 1', *International Journal for Hybrid Microelectronics*, vol. 8, no. 3, pp. 14–30.

Davis, E. M., W. E. Harding, R. S. Schwartz and J. J. Corning (1964), 'Solid Logic Technology: Versatile, High-Performance', *IBM Journal*, April, pp. 102-14.

2 Screens and printing

2.1 Printing

The key to the thick-film process is the printing, for the function of the printer is to take the bulk paste and place a measured amount in the correct position on the substrate. It must do this consistently throughout a run so that there are repeatable results and there is, therefore, the potential of high circuit yields (Du Pont, 1970).

Figure 2.1 shows the basic parts of a printer, while Figure 2.2 shows a typical printer. It consists of:

1. the screen which determines not only where the paste is to be printed, but also largely determines the amount of paste printed;
2. the squeegee which forces the paste through the screen;
3. the substrate holder;
4. an associated pneumatic, vacuum and/or hydraulic system that operates the printer;
5. a heavy frame that holds all the elements and allows them to be adjusted and accurately aligned in position.

We will consider each component in turn.

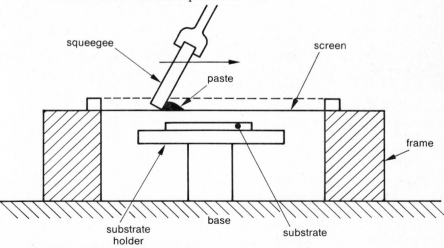

Figure 2.1 Elements of a thick-film printer

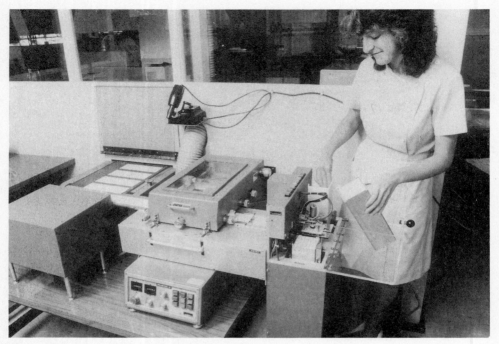

Figure 2.2 Screen printer with automatic feed
Source: With permission from Plessey Australia.

2.2   Screens

The function of the screen is to define the pattern to be printed and meter the amount (thickness) of paste to be deposited. As shown in Figure 2.3, it consists of a strong frame, normally cast aluminium, which has been machined square and across which the screen proper (normally a woven mesh) is stretched. The important properties of the screen mesh are:

1. the material;
2. the size;
3. the tension;
4. the orientation; and
5. the uniformity.

Three common mesh materials are available—polyester, nylon and stainless steel.
    The properties of flexibility (to maintain contact with uneven substrate surfaces, yet not too elastic to produce elongated images), hardness (which affects squeegee life), non-stickability (to substrates), etc., must all be considered for thick-film printing. Not only do they affect the quality of print but also the size of the total print area. Table 2.1 presents the properties of the three materials.

Figure 2.3 Close-up of a screen showing mesh and pattern to be printed superimposed on the screen

Source: With permission from Philips Australia.

Stainless steel provides the highest standard of definition and registration and allows the printing of thick films. It is, however, only suitable for a relatively small print area. Polyester gives low squeegee wear and maintains a good control of print deposits over long runs. Nylon, because of its extra flexibility, gives the poorest performance, yet this extra flexibility can be advantageous in accommodating the varying thickness across a substrate where many printing layers are used (Hargrave, 1983).

Since the mesh material is woven, it can come in various grades. The mesh is categorized by a mesh count which is the number of fibers per inch or centimeter. However, there are other important parameters, such as fiber diameter, mesh aperture and mesh thickness. The fiber diameter and mesh aperture determine the percentage of open area through which a paste can pass. These terms are defined in Figure 2.4. Unfortunately, the various materials come in different fiber diameters so that if a mesh count is given it will be for a particular material. Should one of the other materials be required, an approximate equivalent must be used. For example, many manufacturers use a 200 mesh (fibers/inch) for general work. This is a stainless steel screen. The nearest equivalent in polyester is 196 and in nylon 186. With reference to Figure 2.4, the percentage open area of a screen is given by:

$$\text{Percentage open area} = \frac{100A^2}{(A + D)^2}$$

Parameter	Material		
	Polyester	*Stainless steel*	*Nylon*
Elasticity	Medium	Low	High
Printing properties	Good contact of substrate area	Good contact if small area	Tends to stick to substrate. Don't use viscous pastes
Resiliance (spring back)	High	Low	Low
Thickness printing	Low–Medium	Low–High	Low–Medium
Life	Long	Very long	Medium
Registration definition	Good	Excellent	Poor
Print area/Screen Area			
Maximum	70%	50%	70%
Typical	10%	10%	10%
Typical separation Screen to substrate	1 mm (40 mil)	0.6 mm (25 mil)	1.5 mm (60 mil)

Table 2.1   Summary of properties of different screen materials

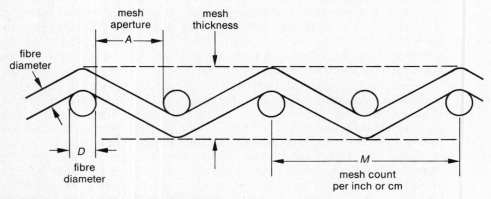

Figure 2.4   Screen construction and terms

Table 2.2 gives some details on common screen meshes. As a general rule, coarse meshes like 160 are used for solder pastes, fine meshes such as 325 for precision work (Bacher, 1986; Gaglani, 1986), while for normal operation a 200 mesh would be used.

Material	Mesh count (inch/cm)	Fibre diam. (microns)	Mesh aperture (microns)	Percentage open area	Mesh thickness (microns)
Stainless steel	80/31	100	224	47	220
	200/77	40	90	48	90
	325/125	30	50	39	67
Polyester	80/31	108	185	39.9	160
	196/77	55	60	27.3	87
	330/130	35	43	30.5	60
Nylon	186/73	60	68	28	98

Table 2.2 Dimensions of mesh materials suitable for screens

The mesh material is uniformly stretched across the frame and fixed with an epoxy glue. Screen tension must be checked and this is normally carried out by applying a known force to the center of the screen and measuring the deflection with a dial gauge (Riemer, 1986). The orientation of the mesh warp and weft to the direction of squeegee stroke (and screen frame) can also vary. The common angles are 90°, 45° and 22.5°. Two factors are important—the strain on the fabric during printing and the resulting interference pattern from the mesh fibers on the printed paste. Maximum flexibility is given when the mesh is at 45°; however, this results in sawtooth edges to printing. Since layouts of thick-film artwork are usually orthogonol, the 90° orientation gives the clearest edges. Yet it is possible for an edge and fiber to coincide so that a narrow strip is completely omitted. As a compromise between these two extremes of 45° and 90°, orientations of 22.5° are sometimes used. If the correct screen count is used to match the performance required, then screen orientation is of no real consequence.

Naturally, for consistent printing over the entire screen, the mesh must be uniform with no defects. Consequently, at purchase and before making up any screen for printing, a screen should be put through a careful inspection procedure. Once a satisfactory screen of the correct mesh count has been selected, the pattern to be printed must be transferred to the screen. Appendix A provides practical information on screen care.

There are three common processes—direct emulsion screen, indirect and direct indirect. In the case of the direct method, the screen mesh is painted, often using an old, hand-held squeegee with the emulsion, making sure that it penetrates the screen, leaving no pin holes. It is leveled on both sides of the screen and allowed to dry for four hours or so (Figure 2.5(a)). New screens can be purchased already coated.

The emulsion used is typically a polyvinyl acetate or polyvinyl alcohol sensitised with a dichromate solution. The screen is then exposed to ultraviolet light through a photographic positive of the correct pattern, making sure that the emulsion side of the photographic positive is in contact with the underside of the screen that would contact the substrate when printing. Those sections exposed polymerize and are made insoluble in water. The unexposed emulsion on the screen can then be washed away and the screen left to dry.

With the indirect emulsion screens, the sensitized emulsion film comes attached to a clear sheet of polyester backing. The film is exposed as described above, making sure on this occasion that the photographic positive emulsion side is in contact with the polyester backing during exposure. After the soluble portions are washed away, the emulsion film with its backing is placed on the underside of the screen and carefully pressed into it with a soft roller.

After six hours or so are allowed for natural drying, the polyester backing sheet can be peeled off. Often this has been forgotten, with the print operator wondering why no printing has occurred on the substrate. Figure 2.5(b) shows the difference in emulsion thickness between the direct and indirect method of screen preparation. In the case of the indirect method, the underside of the emulsion is frequently not flat, but slightly follows the contours of the screen mesh.

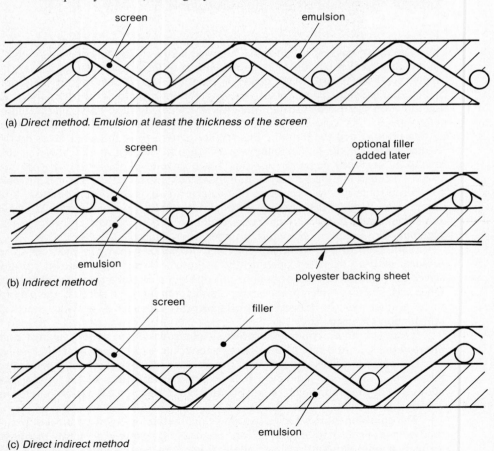

(a) *Direct method. Emulsion at least the thickness of the screen*

(b) *Indirect method*

(c) *Direct indirect method*

Figure 2.5 The three common methods of producing screens for printing

To fill up the inside of the indirect method, and thereby reduce paste waste and simplify screen cleaning, fillers may be purchased and applied. Care must be taken to ensure the filler does not block up portions of the screen where printing must occur.

The direct method generally produces a long-wearing screen and is, therefore, the most suitable method for long production runs. On the other hand, the indirect method is quick and simple and is ideal for prototype runs and research work. There is, however, a difficulty, in that the pushing of the emulsion into the screen after exposure and development can distort the pattern. To overcome this disadvantage, a direct indirect method is employed. Here the sensitized emulsion on its polyester backing, as used in the indirect method, is pressed onto the screen still unexposed. On drying, the backing sheet is removed and it is then exposed as if it were the direct method. A filler is normally used on the inside, if the screen is to be used on production runs.

As previously explained, the type of screen and, particularly, the mesh count have a strong influence on the track width and spacing that can be printed. For extremely fine work (better than 125 microns (5 mil)) etched metal masks may be employed. They offer good thickness control and long screen life; however, they are considerably more expensive to produce. They achieve their precision by dispensing with the mesh fibers at the place of printing, that is, the screen substrate interface. The screens are made from a thin sheet of material such as molybdenum, copper or stainless steel, some 50–75 microns (2–3 mil) thick. It is etched from both sides with a different etch pattern for each side (as shown in Figure 2.6). The side furthest from the substrate is etched to a mesh-type pattern, while the side that contacts the substrate during printing simply has the pattern to be printed. The thin sheet is fixed to a frame for printing. A variation on this process is to etch both sides of the thin sheet with the pattern to be printed and then epoxy the sheet to the underside of a coarse mesh screen (e.g. 80 mesh).

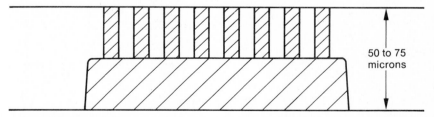

50 to 75 microns

Figure 2.6   Cross-section of an etched metal screen (shaded portion is etched)

Alternative methods of producing fine track widths and spacing are to screen print the whole substrate and etch out the circuit (Gaglani, 1986; Appendix C) or to use the dry resist material that is commonly employed in the printed circuit board industry. Here the dry resist is placed on the substrate, exposed and washed, leaving no resist where printing is to occur. Printing now takes place in the normal way using, say, a 325 mesh screen, but tracks printed are made slightly wider than actually required. This ensures that all regions where there is no photo resist are just covered with paste. After drying, the remaining photo resist is removed together with all excess paste. The paste is then fired.

2.3 Squeegee

The function of the squeegee is to transfer the paste to the substrate (Riemer, 1985). It achieves this by forcing the paste into the screen, surface tension holding the paste to the substrate when the screen separates from the substrate. Thus the squeegee's shape, material and pressure are all critical to ensure long life of squeegee and screen. Compatibility with paste and solvents being screened is also essential.

Typical materials are neoprene, polyurethane and viton with hardnesses in the range 50–65 durometers being optimum. The shape of the squeegee should be such that it has a sharp edge with an angle of attack of 45°–60°. By using a squeegee of rectangular cross-section (as shown in Figure 2.7), then by rotating each of the four edges, improved squeegee life is achieved.

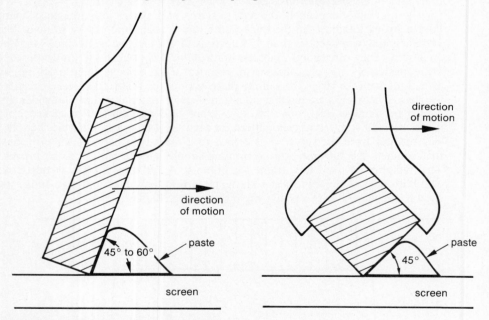

Figure 2.7 Typical squeegee construction

The pressure applied affects the definition of the print. If it is too light, not enough ink is forced through, while if it is too hard then coinage of the screen can occur or the screen is stretched and must be replaced. There is, therefore, an optimum range of pressures for consistent printing results and it is described by an operational characteristic curve as shown in Figure 2.8 (Brown, 1986).

There are two approaches to printing: snap-off and direct contact. The first of these methods must be used with solid metal screens. In the snap-off method, a clearance between the bottom of the screen and substrate surface of about 0.5 mm (20–25 mil) is set (see Table 2.1). It is called the snap-off distance. The squeegee

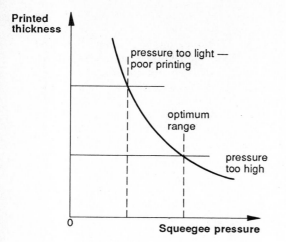

Printed thickness

pressure too light — poor printing

optimum range

pressure too high

0

Squeegee pressure

Figure 2.8 Operational characteristic curve to establish correct squeegee pressure for optimum line defintion and print thickness

stretches the screen to come in contact with the substrate surface so that, on passing on, the screen snaps back. This is illustrated in Figure 2.9(a). Note that on the return stroke a float or flood blade may be used to return the paste. On simple printers, the adhesion between the paste and squeegee may be sufficient to return the paste. With the direct contact method, as illustrated in Figure 2.9(b), the substrate moves up to contact the screen during printing. Thus the screen does not have to stretch.

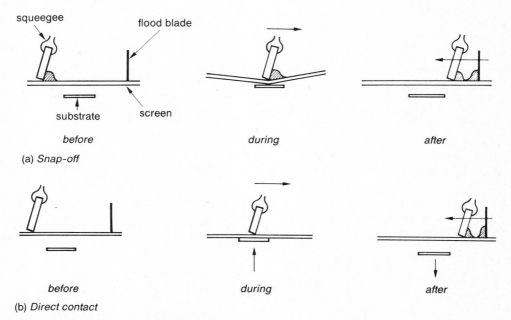

squeegee

flood blade

substrate   screen

before   *during*   *after*

(a) *Snap-off*

before   *during*   *after*

(b) *Direct contact*

Figure 2.9 Diagrammatic presentation of the two printing methods

In either case, the squeegee fills the screen with ink and, on the parting of the screen and substrate, surface tension holds the paste to the substrate (Figure 2.10). Typical thickness of the printed paste may be 12–25 microns (0.5–1 mil). Since the sheet resistance calculations depend on uniform and consistent thickness, this dimension is critical. Many factors affect it, including ink rheology, substrate surface properties, screen preparation, as well as squeegee operation. For example, the quality of a substrate surface can be resolved into at least three components— roughness for the extremely fine variations, waviness for larger variations, and flatness for still larger. Camber or bow is often used as a special case of flatness.

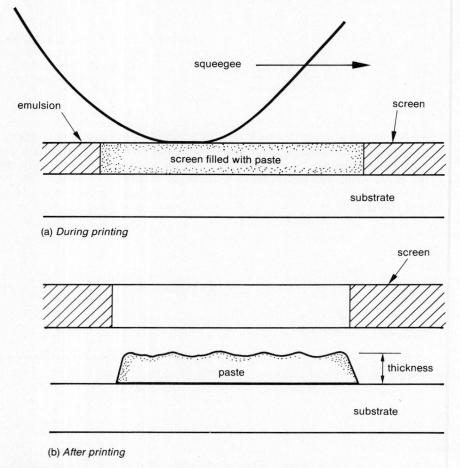

(a) *During printing*

(b) *After printing*

Figure 2.10   The screen meters the paste printed on the substrate

Most substrate suppliers specify only two parameters—roughness and camber (Figure 2.11). To achieve good adhesion of the paste, a roughness of 0.5 micron (0.02 mil) is required, while a camber less than 4 microns/mm (4 mil/inch) is necessary for a consistent printing thickness.

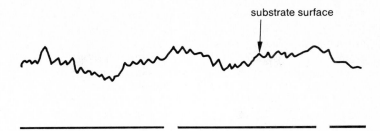

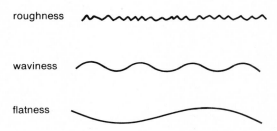

(a) *Substrate surface resolved into three components*

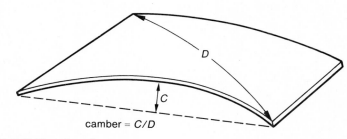

camber = C/D

(b) *Definition of camber*

Figure 2.11 Substrate finish terms

Of all the parameters, paste rheology is the most complex and important. The forcing of the paste through the screen requires that it be a fluid, yet once on the substrate the paste must be near solid so that it will stay as printed and not run. Further, the surface tension must be such that during snap-off the paste adheres to the substrate rather than the screen. This property of changing viscosity (change in shear force to cause a unit change in shear rate) is called 'shear thinning', that is, the viscosity decreases with increasing shear force. Figure 2.12(a) illustrates the behavior of several types of fluids. The classical or Newtonian fluid has constant viscosity. With the dilatant we have the opposite effect to what is required, while pseudoplastic and thixotropic both show shear thinning, with the latter also having hysteresis effects. Thus, thick-film pastes must be pseudoplastic or thixotropic.

If one examines the change of viscosity during printing (Figure 2.12(b)), then as the squeegee applies pressure to move the paste across the screen, the viscosity starts to fall. It reaches a minimum as the paste goes through the screen. Once on the substrate and allowed to settle or level, the viscosity rises gradually, returning to its original value.

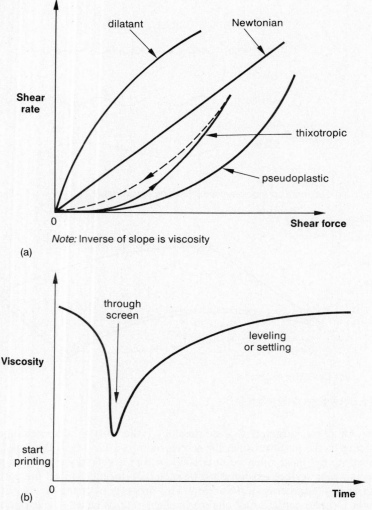

Figure 2.12 Behavioral properties of fluids, including thick-film pastes, during printing

The measurement of paste viscosity is a difficult task. Paste manufacturers usually quote a figure measured on a large batch using a Brookfield viscometer. Many thick-film circuit manufacturers purchase only small quantities of a paste, so that even if one has the Brookfield instrument, having a shear thinning paste in a small jar makes measurement impossible. One way to overcome this is to assume that pastes are correct on delivery and that they take a reading under your own specified conditions. For example, a particular shaft can be used, but inserted only 10 mm (0.4 inch) into the paste. This can be used as a check reading for the life of that paste.

Should the paste viscosity be incorrect, line widening and bleed-out on the edges can occur if it is too low, while scalloped edges, marks or broken lines suggest it is too high in viscosity. Thinning agents such as pine oil are available from paste manufacturers.

2.4   The substrate holder

The substrate holder must perform several functions in addition to simply holding the substrate. It must allow fine and coarse movement of the substrate so that the layer being printed can be correctly aligned with those previously printed, allow release of the substrate after the printing stroke, and protect the screen to prevent coining.

Normally a vacuum hold system is used with an eccentric screw to raise the substrate for removal after printing. Alignment of the screens can be undertaken in the printer or externally on a light chase, depending on the printer model and manufacturer. In the former case, all alignment must be done by shifting the substrate with the appropriate micrometers. In the latter case, the screen sits in a larger holder with a sloppy fit. Using a light chase, the pattern to be printed on the screen is accurately positioned and then locked into place. The holder/screen combination is accurately positioned on pins in the printer. Only minor movements, if any, are needed of the substrate holder to correct any misalignment.

The substrate is normally recessed into the substrate holder to the depth of the substrate thickness, so that the surface of the holder and substrate are at the same level. This means that if the squeegee is slightly too heavy a pressure, coining on the edge of the substrate will not normally occur as the substrate holder prevents the screen from going below the edge of the substrate.

2.5   Operation and frame

To achieve consistent printing, an automatic, non-manual process is required. Consequently, a pneumatic (or hydraulic) system is used to operate the squeegee and flood blade and to move the substrate in and out. The stroke distance, angles, etc., must all be carefully set up, but once correct then reliable, consistent printing will result. Electrically driven belts may even be used to supply substrates to the printer and automatically remove them for subsequent processes. All of this assumes that the printer has a solid frame so that vibration and violent movement by plungers and solenoids will not affect settings or the operation.

2.6   Film thickness measurement

Because the final sheet resistance of a conductor or resistor paste is inversely proportional to film thickness, it is essential that paste thickness be monitored and controlled. Most paste manufacturers give on the data sheets the final paste thickness after firing. To minimize defect numbers, it is preferable to make thickness measurement checks as early as possible in the process, that is, after printing and drying, rather than waiting until firing has occurred. If a paste manufacturer's instructions are followed, then depending on the paste type, the thickness normally will be in the range of 8–25 microns (0.3–1 mil) when firing is complete. During firing, residual solvents and organic material are removed and the paste thickness shrinks by a factor of $\frac{2}{3}-\frac{1}{2}$. Consequently the thickness of a paste after printing and drying may be in the range of 12–40 microns. The exact relationship for any given paste type and process must be determined experimentally.

Non-destructive thickness measurements can be categorized into two groups, approximate and detailed. The first category used for quick checks includes dial gauges (sensitivities available up to 1 micron/devision) and microscope techniques. For example, by refocusing the microscope alternatively on the substrate and paste surfaces, the distance the microscope platform is moved can be read from the platform micrometer. Multiple readings will increase accuracy. The detailed measurements normally involve surface roughness equipment as found in metrology laboratories. Small portable units or large fixtures like the Tally Surf pull a scribe across the substrate and paste surface, giving an accurate scaled plot of the paste profile.

2.7   Thick-film writing machines

A development by STC England, and, more recently, by Micropen in the United States, is a direct writing stylus (Nayak et al., 1986). Its operation is similar to a digital plotter except the substrate moves rather than the pen. The pen is a copper stylus with a diamond follower insert which sets the distance the stylus is from the substrate, typically 25 microns. Compressed air forces a paste from the stylus. The minimum track width printed depends on the stylus hole diameter (about 50 microns), air pressure, speed of the table and viscosity of the paste. Shading is used to fill in an area. The writing machine is an ideal tool in the development of prototyping circuits.

2.8   Exercises

1. Two 200/77 stainless steel meshes are available as given in Table 2.3. What differences could you expect if they were used for printing?

Wire diameter (microns)	Mesh aperture (microns)	Fabric thickness (microns)
40	90	90
50	80	110

Table 2.3 Exercise 1

2. Devise an alignment system using a light chase external to the printer to ensure that each layer of printing is correctly aligned with respect to each other, if:
(a) there are to be alignment marks printed on the substrate;
(b) there are to be no alignment marks printed on the substrate.

3. Figure 2.13 shows the ideal shape that should have been printed and a series of actual shapes. What do you think is wrong in each case?

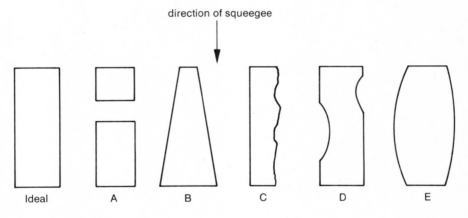

Figure 2.13 Exercise 3

2.9   References

Bacher, R. J. (1986), 'High Resolution Thick Film Printing', *Proc. 1986 International Symposium on Microelectronics*, 6–8 October, Atlanta, Ga, pp. 576–81.

Brown, D. O. (1986), 'Screen Printing–An Integrated System', *Proc. 1986 International Symposium on Microelectronics*, 6–8 October, Atlanta, Ga, pp. 582–90.

Du Pont (1970), *The Thick Film Microcircuitry Handbook*, Du Pont Electronic Products, Wilmington, De.

Gaglani J. A. (1986), 'Obtaining Fine Line Geometries in Today's Hybrids', *Proc. 1986 International Symposium on Microelectronics*, 6–8 October, Atlanta, Ga, pp. 819–25.

Hargrave, C. E. (1983), 'Thick Film Screen Techniques', *Hybrid Circuits*, no. 2, Spring, pp. 21–7.

Nayak, D., L. Hwang and A. Reisman (1986), 'Evaluation of a CAD/CAM System for Direct Writing of Thick Film Conductors, Resistors and Capacitors', *Proc. 1986 International Symposium on Microelectronics*, 6–8 October, Atlanta, Ga, pp. 775–83.

Riemer, D. E. (1985) 'Ink Hydrodynamics of Screen Printing', *Proc. 1985 International Symposium on Microelectronics*, 11–14 November 1985, Anaheim, Cal., pp. 52–8.

Riemer, D. E. (1986), 'The Function and Performance of the Stainless Steel Screen During the Screen Ink Transfer Process', *Proc. 1986 International Symposium on Microelectronics*, 6–8 October, Atlanta, Ga, pp. 826–31.

3 Paste and substrate material systems

3.1 Introduction

With the passage of time, new paste and substrate materials are constantly being developed. It is, therefore, somewhat difficult to categorize them. For example, the different substrate types could form the basis of categorizing the thick-film systems, that is, ceramic, steel and resin-based types. However, this would exclude special substrate types and, further, pastes designed for resin-based substrates can equally well be printed on higher temperature substrates like alumina. Thus, the method of categorizing selected is in terms of paste rather than substrate types.

There are two main families of pastes—noble and base metal types. Further divisions are possible of the noble metal types into high, medium and low firing temperature types, as illustrated in Figure 3.1. Normally as the firing temperature of the paste system decreases so does the system's maximum operating temperature and performance. At present, only the high temperature system is adequate for military and good professional products.

Before considering in detail each of the systems, mention must be made of the paste types required to make a thick-film circuit. These can be classified as follows:

1. conductor pastes having various properties making them useful for soldering, bonding, etc.;

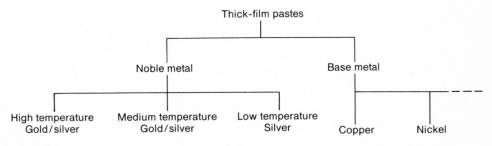

Figure 3.1   Summary of thick-film paste systems

2. resistor pastes of various sheet resistances;
3. dielectric pastes of differing dielectric constants and frequency properties (a special category here is the crossover paste that forms the insulating layer between two crossing conductor tracks);
4. coating pastes to protect the final circuit (these may be an epoxy or glass type);
5. solder pastes;
6. special pastes (these include ferrite pastes for inductors, thermistor pastes, voltage-dependent pastes showing switching characteristics, etc.).

An important part of the system is the substrate. Not only does it mechanically support the circuit components, it must also give mechanical protection of the components, help dissipate heat and provide high electrical insulation and isolation. In general, substrates should have the following properties:

1. high strength;
2. high abrasion resistance;
3. ability to withstand paste firing temperature;
4. dimensional stability;
5. correct surface finish;
6. good electrical resistance;
7. low dielectric constant;
8. chemical stability and compatibility with pastes;
9. thermal expansion matching devices mounted and printed on it;
10. good thermal conductivity;
11. be machinable;
12. low porosity;
13. low cost.

3.2   Noble metal based paste systems

As the name suggests these pastes include one or more noble metals. The early pastes were based on the silver-palladium combination and this mixture is still employed today. The exact compositions of pastes are company secrets, but by and large they consist of combinations of the following:

1. noble metals;
2. insulating material such as glass frit;
3. an organic vehicle to hold the mixture together for printing;
4. special additives to improve performance.

3.2.1   The high temperature pastes

The composition of these pastes (Hamer and Biggers, 1973) follows the list given previously. Since they consist of a mixture of metal and metal oxides they are often called cermet pastes. The noble metals are in finely ground particle form, typically 10 microns in size. The metals are typically silver, gold, palladium, ruthenium and platinum or combinations of these.

Perhaps the most common conductor pastes are based on the silver-palladium combination, silver providing good conductivity and the palladium helping to reduce both cost and the problem of silver migration. Too much palladium results in poor solderability and increased conductor resistance.

The metals themselves do not adhere well to the substrate surface. Two methods are available to overcome this difficulty. First, glass frit can be mixed into the paste. It is usually a borosilicate glass. A typical mixture is given in Table 3.1.

Oxide material	Percentage by weight
Lead	30
Boron	35
Silicon	10
Bismuth	25

Table 3.1 Composition of a borosilicate glass frit

On firing, the glass softens and wets the substrate. It concentrates, therefore, at the substrate surface, trapping the metal powder which sinters. Since the glass does not chemically bond to the metal or substrate, adhesion depends on the mechanical linkage of the glass and, therefore, a mechanical bond is formed. Conductor pastes employing this bond mechanism are called 'fritted'. The bond is illustrated in Figure 3.2.

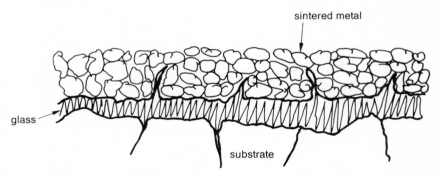

Figure 3.2 Enlarged cross-section of a conductor paste based on the use of glass frit and noble metals

In the second approach, special additives such as cadmium, copper and copper oxide are included to give a reactive bond. Here, if an alumina substrate is used, copper aluminate and other compounds are formed at the substrate surface. How good the adhesion is depends upon the substrate–impurities. Typically, the alumina is only 94–96 percent pure. Should the impurities be calcium and barium silicates, then weaker reactive bonding occurs than if the impurities had been magnesium silicate. Conductor pastes using this bond mechanism are called 'reactive bonding' or 'fritless'.

A third class of conductor paste exists where both of the above methods are combined. They are called 'mixed bonded'.

The organic material consists of a binder, usually ethyl cellulose, and a solvent, typically pine oil or butyl cellulose acetate. Their function is to hold the mixture together until printing is finished. The volatile portion is heated off after printing (drying) while the organic material is burnt off during firing in the furnace. Because pastes contain these volatile materials, to minimize evaporation it is customary to store pastes in a refrigerator at near zero (°C) temperature.

With a resistor material, a wide range of sheet resistance values are required. Since most high bulk resistivity materials are semiconductors, with a high temperature coefficient, they are by themselves unacceptable as a paste material. Suspending small particles of good conductors in a glass full of coarser particle size also gives an unsatisfactory solution. The resultant chain structure, as illustrated in Figure 3.3(a), is uncontrollable as the change from high to low resistivity occurs over a very small change in metal percentage by weight (Figure 3.3(b)).

The solution adopted by most paste manufacturers is to add what is called a 'resistor pigment' in particulate form to a glass frit, the latter normally being a lead borosilicate glass. Here the conductor is made to react with the other materials, including the glass, to give a more controlled change in resistivity with percentage pigment by weight (Figure 3.3(b)). Such pastes are called 'reactive'. The original Du Pont resistor pigment consisted of a silver-palladium mix. During firing, areas of palladium oxide, a P-type semiconductor, and silver-palladium alloy are formed in the glass, the former being the dominant material in the conducting chain in determining the sheet resistance. The silver was added to improve the low resistance characteristics, but unfortunately gives a high temperature coefficient of resistance. The palladium system is also sensitive to firing temperature and is therefore no longer used.

While other precious metal oxides such as thallium, iridium and molybdenum could be used as resistor pigments, the most common material today is ruthenium.

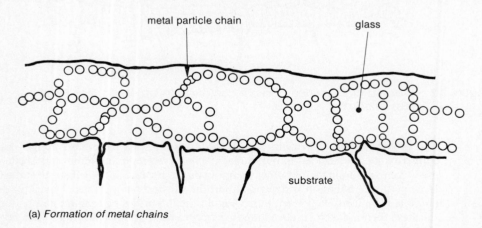

(a) *Formation of metal chains*

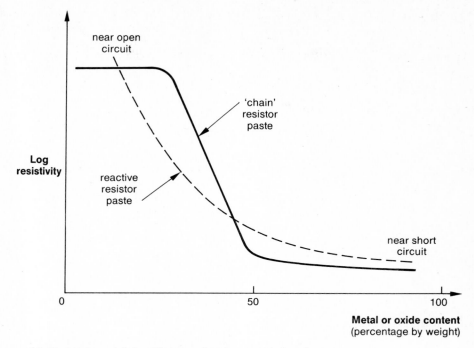

(b) *Change in resistivity with percentage increase in metal*

Figure 3.3   Properties of resistor pastes

When used on their own, ruthenium dioxide resistors have a large positive temperature coefficient of resistance and additives such as niobium pentoxide are used to help correct this. A considerable improvement in electrical performance is achieved if more complex oxides of ruthenium are used. An example is the pyrochlorate structure, bismuth ruthenate ($Bi_2Ru_2O_7$), one of a series of oxides of ruthenium that exhibit metallic conductivity.

With today's reactive resistor pastes, the major part of the resistance is due to the mechanism of charge transport through conductor networks formed by conducting particles separated by thin glass layers. Conduction across the glass layer is believed to be by both tunneling and thermal excitation (Chen and Cottle, 1986).

Dielectric paste can be formed simply by omitting the metals and using the remaining glass frit. Unfortunately, the glass has a low firing temperature and at higher temperatures, required for firing upper conducting layers, the glass becomes too fluid. Two solutions are available to overcome this difficulty, resulting in two types of dielectrics:

1. ceramic loaded glasses;
2. recrystallizing (devitrifying) glasses.

In the first case, the glass is loaded with ceramic powders such as aluminum oxide or zirconium dioxide. On firing, the viscosity of the molten glass increases rapidly, as it wets and then begins to dissolve the ceramic. Sintering results.

With recrystallizing glasses, the glass initially melts. However, at a higher temperature nucleation occurs and a more crystalline phase quickly precipitates out. This new glass phase does not melt during any further firing steps. This type of glass is going out of favor because reactions between it and resistor pastes printed on top cause large changes in sheet resistance values.

For crossovers the dielectric material needs to have a low dielectric constant to minimize coupling. For capacitors, a high dielectric constant per unit area is often required to minimize capacitor area. Additives such as titanium dioxide can be used to increase the dielectric constant. However, the resultant dielectric constant is limited by the glass and any air voids present.

These high temperature paste families are typically fired at temperatures from $750°$–$850°C$, the exact temperature depending on the paste composition. Platinum conductors and some dielectric pastes may even require temperatures greater than $950°C$. Consequently, the substrate materials for these pastes must be able to withstand these high temperatures.

Several materials meet these requirements and they include alumina, beryllia, titanates and, more recently, aluminum nitride. Of these, alumina is almost universally employed, with beryllia used in special cases to allow higher dissipation. Unfortunately, special safety standards and precautions must be adhered to when it is used. Table 3.2 compares typical properties of the two materials.

Property	Alumina	Beryllia	Unit
Surface roughness	<0.6	<0.6	microns
Thermal conductivity	26	390	W/m.K
Coefficient of linear thermal expansion	6.2	7.0	$10^{-6}/°C$
Dielectric strength	12	12	kV/mm
Volume resistivity	$>10^{14}$	$>10^{14}$	ohm/cm
Dielectric constant	9	7	
Dissipation factor	0.0004	0.001	

Table 3.2 Properties of high temperature substrate materials

The alumina substrates are typically 94–96 percent aluminum oxide (Table 3.3) and come in a variety of thickness with 625 microns (25 mil) and 1000 microns (40 mil) being the most common. Pigments may be added to color the substrate pink, black, etc., but its normal color is white. Figure 3.4 shows a range of alumina substrates with various scribed patterns.

The substrates are made (Hamer and Biggers, 1973) by sintering alumina powders at very high temperatures. Fluxes such as magnesium oxide, calcium oxide or silicon dioxide (Table 3.3) are added to reduce the sintering temperature. The powders are mixed and then ball ground to a fine particle size. Water is added

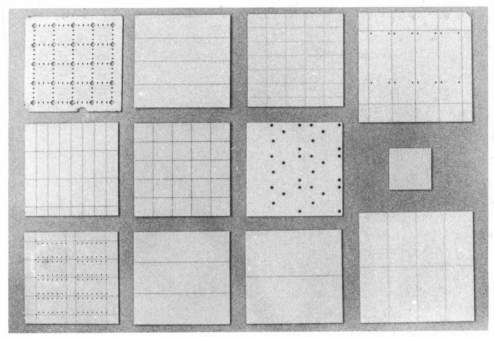

Figure 3.4 Alumina substrates with various scribed patterns prior to printing
Source: With permission from Philips Australia.

Component	US 1	US 2	Japan 1	Japan 2	UK 1	UK 2
Al_2O_3	94.67	95.10	95.25	95.05	97.31	97.02
SiO_2	2.98	2.33	3.38	3.30	1.71	1.97
CaO	0.20	0.01	0.02	0.04	0.84	1.00
MgO	2.15	1.94	1.35	1.61	0.14	0.14

Table 3.3 Compositions in percentage weight of various alumina substrates

Note: The first four are based on a magnesium silicate flux while the last two on calcium silicate.

Source: Coleman (1976), 'Evaluation of Thick-Film Conductors', *Proc. 1976 International Microelectronics Conference*, 19–21 October, Brighton, UK.

to help the mixing. The resultant slurry is either dried and pressed into the desired shape or poured onto a flat glass bed and allowed to dry.

This green substrate can be scored deeply (or punched) so that it can be snapped and broken into a desired size. This allows many circuits to be printed simultaneously on a large substrate and, after processing, broken into the individual substrates (often called biscuits). After scoring or pressing, the green substrate is then fired at around 1700°C and sintering occurs.

As an alternative to scoring green substrates, laser scoring of fired substrates is now widely used, before and after printing.

Substrate sizes can vary from 10 mm square to larger than Eurocard size. Typical sizes in use are 1 × 1 inch, 1 × 2 inch and 2 × 2 inch.

3.2.2 Medium temperature pastes and substrates

This system came about in an attempt to reduce the cost of consumer products that required electronics. For example, the white goods range such as washers, refrigerators, etc. Since the thick-film electronics need only be printed on to an insulating material, why not use the enamel-coated steel, used to house and/or strengthen the product, as the substrate. Procelain-coated steel substrates and appropriate pastes have been under development for more than a decade (Stein et al., 1979a), but have still not proved popular. One reason for this is that the sodium in the early enamels badly affected the long-term properties of the thick-film pastes. However, companies such as RCA (*RCA Review*, 1981) have developed total porcelain enamel steel systems that can cope with leaded and surface-mounted components on substrates up to 18 × 24 inch in size. The steel is predrilled and punched before it is coated with enamel.

The manufacture of the substrate is as follows. The enamel consists of an acidic refractory material such as quartz, feldspar or clay reacted with a flux such as borax, soda ash, cryolite or fluorspar to form a glass. This glass is melted, fritted and ball milled in water. Pigments may be added and usually some cobalt ($<\frac{1}{2}$ percent) to improve the adhesion to the steel.

The enamel must have a melting point temperature high enough so that it does not melt when the thick films are fired, yet low enough to minimize oxidation and warping of the steel during coating. Since glass is relatively weak in tensile strength the enamel is designed to have a higher thermal expansion characteristic than the steel in order to keep the glass in compression.

For electronic grade substrates, extra low carbon (<0.003 percent) steel is used. It is cleaned, acid pickled to remove surface oxides and plated with nickel in an electroless nickel-plating solution. The glass powder is applied to the steel by either dipping or spraying (normal or electrostatic). After drying, the coated steel is fired for a few minutes at 800°–900°C. The resultant steel substrate is denser and stronger than the high and low temperature system types. Figure 3.5 shows a typical cross section while Table 3.4 gives properties.

Property	Value	Unit
Tensile strength	3200	kg/cm^2
Coefficient of linear thermal expansion	6–7	ppm/°C
Thermal conductivity glass	1.25	W/m.K
Thermal conductivity steel	80	W/m.K
Dielectric constituents (enamels)	8–22	—
Maximum processing temperature	675	°C

Table 3.4 Typical properties of porcelain enamel-coated steel

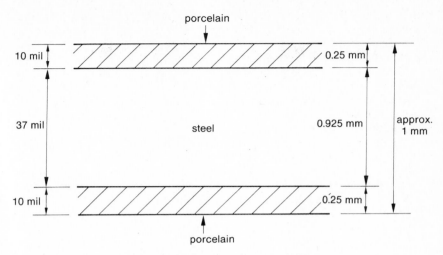

Figure 3.5   Cross-section of a porcelain enamel steel substrate

Recently, other steel substrate systems have been developed. The surfaces are roughened by oxidation so that a dielectric paste can be printed directly on top of it. The thick-film circuit can then be printed on to this dielectric coating. The substrates can be purchased with the dielectric paste coating already on it.

Examples of these new materials are:

1. Fecralloy—an iron, chromium, aluminium composition with yttrium added to it.
2. Sicromal—a stainless steel also with yttrium additives. It has a very low linear thermal coefficient of expansion.

The pastes used for these substrates are very similar to high temperature pastes previously discussed but designed to fire at 625°C (Allington and Coté, 1978; Stein et al., 1979b). The most common series of resistor pastes are ruthenium based.

3.2.3   Low temperature pastes and substrates

These pastes were designed to be compatible with the printed wiring board industry and can be printed on any material that can withstand 150°C for two or three hours (Stein et al., 1979b; Johnson, 1982a, 1982b). Many materials based on plastics and even cardboard or paper can be employed as the substrates. Naturally, the medium and high temperature substrates already discussed can be employed as well.

Since plastic membranes can now be used as the substrates, the range of applications of thick-film circuits can be expanded to include touch switches, automobile flexible electronic wiring boards, sensitive small pressure transducers, etc. The printing can even be done on a continuous roll substrate which is later punched into the required piece parts. Predrilled or punched holes allow printed-through holes. Here a vacuum system pulls the paste through these holes during printing. Printed circuit cards as large as 24 × 24 inch have been used for substrates.

The pastes used in this system are all polymer based. There are two basic types. The first is the thermoplastic type where the paste is kept in liquid form by a solvent. These materials soften on heating and so have a lower maximum operating temperature, which is still suitable for consumer products. Curing is normally by solvent evaporation at 70°–125°C using infrared heating. These pastes are normally silver based and of a conductive type only. Their main application is membrane switches.

Thermosetting paste is the second type. These pastes are thermally fired at 150°C for typically 2–3 hours. Increasing the temperature to 180°C is possible to reduce the time, but often the substrate material will not allow this. The viscosity of the paste is controlled by either a solvent or a functional dilutant (monomer) which is often the additive that decides the paste function, be it a conductor, resistor or dielectric type. The solvent is evaporated during curing, whereas the monomer becomes part of the polymer during cross-linking. Additives to the thermoplastic pastes are in finely ground particle form and are held in suspension by mechanical mixing. Although infrared curing is normally used, ultraviolet methods are being explored as the curing times are considerably reduced.

The advantages of the thermosetting pastes are their resistance to solvents, low current noise, high wear resistance (suitable for potentiometers) and low costs. Three types of paste are available:

1. *Conductors.* Additives to the polymer include silver, copper and nickel with silver being the usual. The printed conductors can be electroplated on and, with care, some can even be soldered to.
2. *Resistors.* Carbon (graphite or carbon black) is used as a functional dilutant, the ohms per square depending on the amount of carbon loading. For resistors less than 1 kohm per square, silver is also added.
3. *Dielectric.* No additive need be added as the polymer is an insulator. However, to increase the dielectric constant, fillers such as alumina are used.

3.3   Base-metal paste and substrates

The upward movement in the price of noble metals has forced manufacturers to look for less expensive materials. Copper is an obvious choice for it has a resistivity less than either silver or gold, but has the problems of oxidization and as a rule cannot be directly soldered or wire bonded to. This is true for all base-metal conductor pastes, whether they are copper, nickel, chromium or aluminum (Stein et al., 1980).

At this time, only the copper system has been developed to the point where it can be used in products. To prevent oxidization, a nitrogen atmosphere furnace is used. Since there is no oxygen, for it must be kept less than 10 ppm, the organic binder cannot be burnt off, and different binders that are removed by thermal cracking must be employed. The resultant products must be exhausted from the furnace before firing of the copper occurs. Peak firing temperatures of 900°C are typical (Bloom and Kuo, 1985).

3.4 Paste and system selection

Of the various systems discussed thus far, the high temperature, noble-metal system is universally used. This is followed by the low temperature, polymer-paste system which is growing rapidly in some areas. The medium temperature porcelain/steel substrate and base-metal systems tend to be more in the research area. However, some organizations state that they are using or are about to use them in products. The choice at present is mainly between the most expensive noble-metal system which offers excellent performance and the low-cost polymer system with reduced performance, which is still very acceptable in many consumer and professional products. No matter which system is selected, there is still the decision as to what paste type to use. Only conductor, resistor and dielectric pastes will be considered.

3.4.1 Selection of conductor pastes

When selecting a conductor paste for a system, the following factors must be considered.

1. *Conductivity*. The sheet resistance of the various pastes can vary by almost two orders of magnitudes. Table 3.5 gives typical values.

Conductor material	Sheet resistance (milliohm/square)
Copper	1.5
Silver platinum	2.0
Gold	3.0
Silver palladium	30
Gold palladium	50

Table 3.5 Comparison sheet resistance of various conductor pastes

Source: F. N. Sinnadurai (1985), *Handbook of Microelectronics Packaging and Interconnection Technologies*, Electrochemical Publication, Ayre, Scotland.

2. *Firing temperature*. Some furnaces have an upper temperature limit of about 850°C, above which the belt starts shedding excessive particles. Compatibility with other pastes is also important. For example, with a capacitor the second conductor firing must occur after firing the dielectric paste.
3. *Cofiring*. Some pastes allow resistors and conductors to be cofired without degradation (appreciable) of resistor performance.
4. *Connection method*. Normally soldering or wire bonds are the alternatives. Some pastes suitable for soldering require special silver-loaded (approximately 0.5 percent silver) solder to ensure that during soldering the tin does not leach the silver. Some pastes cannot be soldered, for example, if the platinum content is high.

5. *Compatibility*. The conductor paste must be compatible with other pastes to be used. Normally one stays within a given family; however, there are exceptions. For example, palladium-silver conductors can be used with both ruthenium and carbon polymer resistors.

6. *Migration*. Silver pastes suffer badly from migration, particularly in very humid conditions. The silver ions migrate toward the negative potential, forming dendrites which eventually cause a short between tracks. The growth rate is given by:

$$G = EFe^{-\epsilon/kT}$$

where:
> G is the growth rate in microns/sec
> E is the applied electric field
> T is the temperature in $^\circ$K
> F is a function of the geometric shape and process (e.g. firing temperature)
> k is Boltzman's constant
> ϵ is the activation energy $= 1.15 \pm 0.15$ eV

The addition of palladium and platinum reduce silver migration but it still may be a problem. Gold does not suffer from this migration.

7. *Printing resolution*. Minimum possible line width that can be printed, using the paste.

8. *Adhesion*. This is the force required to pull the conductor from the substrate. With surface mounting of components, the solder joint/conductor must carry the weight of any large added chip component.

9. *Cost and availability*. This may also include second sourcing.

3.4.2   Selection of resistor pastes

In addition to the factors listed under section 3.4.1, the following should also be added:

1. susceptibility to variations of the firing profile;
2. susceptibility to undergoing multiple firing;
3. repeatability of results;
4. resistor temperature coefficient;
5. resistor voltage coefficient; normally the voltage should be kept less than 150 volts per mm of resistor length (Carcia et al., 1976);
6. the noise generated (normally this is low when compared to that generated by most discrete resistors);
7. range of pastes (this is usually in decade steps, with sheet resistances from 10 ohm to 10 Mohm per square, but with some series the properties of the pastes at the extremities may not be adequate);
8. aging effects of resistors (this may be affected by the packaging method including encapsulants).

3.4.3 Selection of dielectric pastes

Dielectric pastes may be employed for capacitors, crossovers, solder barriers and insulation in multilayer circuits. Requirements for each application will differ. To the factors given in sections 3.4.1 and 3.4.2, the following may need to be considered:

1. *Dielectric constant*. This will determine the physical area occupied by capacitors or coupling in crossovers and multilayer structures.
2. *Frequency response*. Many pastes show dielectric dispersion. The correct paste for the desired frequency range of operation must be selected.
3. *Pin holing*. A good paste should not produce many pin holes that can cause conductor shorts.

3.5 Exercises

1. Examine a manufacturer's data sheet for a conductor paste and try to discover the following information:
   (a) basic ingredients;
   (b) sheet resistance;
   (c) firing temperature range and profile;
   (d) thickness of conductor after printing or firing;
   (e) whether or not cofiring is allowed;
   (f) viscosity of paste and solvent type used;
   (g) shelf life;
   (h) suitability for soldering, wire bonding, plating, or welding.

2. Examine a manufacturer's data sheet for a family of resistor pastes and try to ascertain the following:
   (a) conductor pastes compatible with them;
   (b) sheet resistance range;
   (c) firing temperature and profile;
   (d) average dissipation per square millimeter;
   (e) viscosity of pastes and solvent type used;
   (f) whether or not cofiring is allowed;
   (g) temperature coefficients;
   (h) voltage coefficient and any voltage limitations.

3. Examine a manufacturer's data sheet for a dielectric paste and endeavor to discover the following:
   (a) dielectric constant;
   (b) frequency range use;
   (c) firing temperature and profile;
   (d) conductor paste compatible with them.

4. What special paste products can you discover (e.g. ferrite pastes, thermistor pastes, solder pastes, voltage-dependent pastes, etc.)? Make a list and examine their properties.

3.6 References

Allington, T. R. and R. E. Coté (1978), *Characterization of Thick Film Compositions for Porcelained Steel Substrates*, Du Pont Electronic Materials Division, Wilmington, De, USA.

Bloom, T. R. and C. Y. Kuo (1985), 'A Multilayer Base Metal Thick Film System for Use on High Temperature Porcelainized Steel', *Proc. 1985 International Symposium on Microelectronics*, 11–14 November, Anaheim, Cal., pp. 441–5.

Carcia, P. F., F. J. Anders and R. M. Rosenberg (1976), *High Voltage Characteristics of New High Resistivity Thick Film Resistors*, Du Pont Electronic Materials Division, Wilmington, De, USA.

Coleman, M. V. (1976), 'Evaluation of Thick Film Conductors', *Proc. 1976 International Microelectronics Conference*, 19–21 October, Brighton, UK, pp. 1–15.

Cottle, J. G. and T. M. Chen (1986), 'Physical Model of Burst Noise in Thick Film Resistors', *Solid State Electronics*, vol. 29, no. 9, pp. 865–72.

Hamer, D. W. and J. V. Biggers (1973), *The Fundamentals of Thick-Film Hybrid Technology*, State of the Arts Inc., 1315 South Allen Street, State College, Pa., 16801.

Johnson, R. W. (1982*a*), 'Polymer Thick Film Applications' *Circuits Manufacturing*, vol. 22, no. 9, pp. 44–50.

Johnson, R. W. (1982*b*), 'Polymer Thick Films; Technology and Materials', *Circuits Manufacturing*, vol. 22, no. 7, pp. 54–60.

RCA Review (1981), vol. 42, no. 2, June. Total issue on 'Porcelain Enamel Steel Substrates'.

Sinnadurai, F. N. (1985), *Handbook of Microelectronics Packaging and Interconnection Technologies*, Electrochemical Publications, Ayre, Scotland.

Stein, S. J., C. Huang and L. Cang (1980), *Base Metal Thick Film Conductors*, Electro Science Laboratories, Pennsauken, NJ.

Stein, S. J., C. Huang and A. S. Gelb (1979*a*), *Comparison of Enameled Steel Substrate Properties for Thick Film Use*, Electro Science Laboratories, Pennsauken, NJ.

Stein, S. J., C. Huang and A. S. Gelb (1979*b*), *Thick Film Materials on Porcelain Enameled Steel Substrates*, Electro Science Laboratories, Pennsauken, NJ.

4 The firing and trimming processes

4.1 The remaining screen processing steps

After printing and before packaging, there are several important steps. The first two may seem trivial, but they are important to achieve consistent results. They are paste settling and drying. After printing, the substrates must be left standing for 5–10 minutes to give the paste time to settle so that the screen fiber impressions disappear. Following this, the pastes (apart from the low temperature polymer pastes) are dried to remove the solvents, by heating to 125°–150°C, again for 5–10 minutes. This freezes the printing, so that additional printings or firing of the pastes can follow. In large production facilities, these two steps normally occur automatically by placing the substrates on a moving belt (Figure 4.2(d)).

In the case of polymer pastes, the thermoplastic type need only be heated to a low temperature to drive off the solvent, while the thermosetting plastic is heated to 150°C for hours. They do not require the higher temperature firing. In the case of all other pastes, firing at high temperature in accordance with a specified time/temperature profile is necessary to complete the process. In fact, most unfired pastes are non-conductive and this is one simple test to discover whether or not a substrate has been fired. Subtle color changes may also occur.

4.2 Firing of pastes

Paste manufacturers normally specify a time/temperature profile to which pastes must be fired if their published characteristics are to be achieved. Traditionally, it is based on having a seven-zone belt furnace. However, furnaces with as few as three zones can be used to reduce equipment costs. For research laboratories, moving arm furnaces can be used to cope with the small volume throughout. Here a tube furnace or similar is set to the peak temperature and then the substrates are mechanically moved in and out of the heated area at a rate to achieve the required profile. More recently, in order to reduce furnace costs, infrared lamps have been used to fire pastes.

The firing process is not simply a baking. It is to produce a number of reactions. Consider, for example, the firing of the high temperature noble-metal pastes. A typical time/temperature profile is given in Figure 4.1.

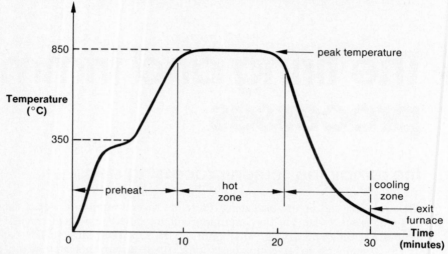

Figure 4.1   Typical time/temperature profile for firing thick-film pastes

The profile has three regions. The preheat region has a definite kink in it at a temperature in the range of 300°–350°C where burning out of the organic vehicle occurs. This must not occur at too violent a rate else bubbling, cracking or blistering of the paste surface may occur. If not all of the organic material is removed, then the paste properties can be severely affected (e.g. low sheet resistance and poor ageing characteristics).

In the hot zone, a balance is established between the amount of metal and metal oxide in the fired resistor paste composition. It is a reversible process, the final percentages depending upon the oven temperature, time in the hot zone and amount of oxygen present. If there is insufficient time, temperature or oxygen, there will be a greater percentage of metal and, therefore, a lower sheet resistance. Conductor pastes are not too critical, but resistor pastes can be. Consequently, it is desirable to plan a process so that resistor pastes are one of the last, if not the last, paste to be printed and fired.

The amount of metal oxide present also depends upon the amount of impurities present. For example, there must be no chlorinated water in the furnace as metal chlorides will be formed, thereby upsetting the metal/metal oxide balance.

The cooling zone freezes the process and allows the substrate to exit the furnace at near ambient temperature. An exception to the freezing of the process is the use of some crossover and dielectrics pastes where recrystallization occurs.

A typical furnace construction (Hamer and Biggers, 1973) is shown in Figures 4.2 and 4.3. The belt made of steel (<800°C) or nichrome (<1000°C) continuously rotates. Early furnaces were usually inclined at an angle of 2°–3° to allow a flow of air through the furnace, supplying the oxygen for the process.

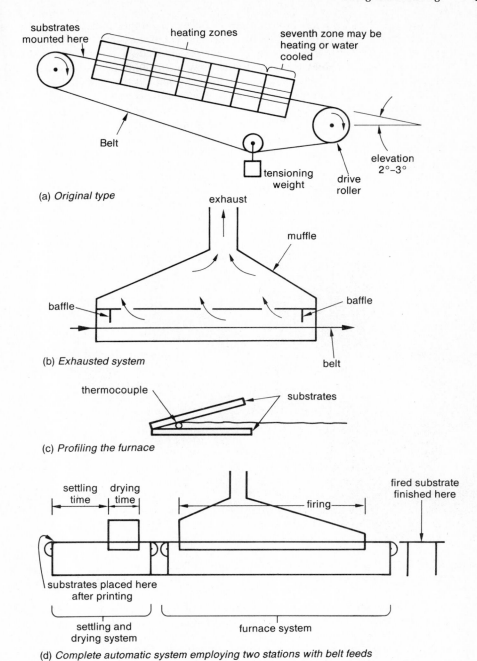

(a) *Original type*

(b) *Exhausted system*

(c) *Profiling the furnace*

(d) *Complete automatic system employing two stations with belt feeds*

Figure 4.2 Furnace for firing substrates

Today it is realized that furnace atmosphere is very important (Delott, 1985) so furnaces now have elaborate pumped inlet and exhaust systems to give controlled air flow, ensuring that burnt-out organic binder residues do not enter the heat zone and the process is repeatable. Baffles may be added to control and restrict the extra air flow caused by the exhaust system, for should the flow be too great the temperature profile can become distorted. The heating zones in a conventional belt furnace employ a resistance heater, a thermocouple temperature sensing element and an electronic controller. To check the profile it is usual to employ a thermocouple sandwiched between two substrates, so that the actual substrate temperature is recorded (Figure 4.2(c)). The output from the thermocouple is fed to a chart recorder.

Figure 4.3   Multizone, controlled atmosphere belt furnace
Source: With permission from Plessey Australia.

Where base metals are being fired in a nitrogen atmosphere (Bradley, 1985), the muffle system must not contain any leaks to admit air for oxygen levels in excess of 10 ppm upset the process by allowing the copper to become oxidized. Nitrogen curtains must be on the entrance and exit. Further, a critical temperature in the process is 500°C, for, if all by-products are not removed before this temperature, they will be carbonized and cause blistering of the fired paste. Figure 4.4 shows a muffler design for a nitrogen furnace.

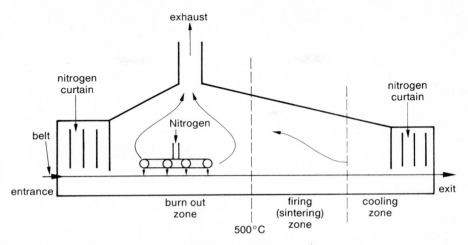

Figure 4.4 Muffle for a nitrogen atmosphere belt furnace

A recent innovation to firing is the use of the infrared lamps instead of conventional resistance heating. While the furnace system is cheaper and more efficient, the amount of information on the properties of pastes fired in this way is small (Rao and Loch, 1985; Smetana, 1985).

4.3 Component trimming

Once the substrate has been fired, components may need to be trimmed. Printing tolerances are typically ± 20 percent and, in many cases, this is not good enough. While components could be trimmed to an extremely low tolerance, there is little to be gained in trimming to an accuracy better than that set by the paste temperature coefficient and ageing properties. In fact, a good compromise is to trim to the tolerance set by these two factors, which is typically ± 1 percent.

Over the years, many methods have evolved to trim components (Singh, 1976), from simple mechanical rotary abraders, to electrochemical trimming (one of the few processes that allowed decreasing a resistance value as well as increasing it), and arc trimming. Two methods are used today—air abrasive and laser trimming.

With abrasive trimming (Figure 4.5), a jet of (dry) air containing a fine abrasive powder such as alumina, of particle size 15–25 microns, is used to abrade away the resistor. The jet is typically 0.5–1 mm in diameter. The substrate to be trimmed is mounted on an xy platform beneath the air jet. The platform is moved in the x and y direction by either a motor-driven lead screw or a pneumatic plunger. A bridge monitors the component value, so that when it reaches the desired set value, the platform movement stops and the air jet switches off. To remove the spent abrasive powder, a vacuum exhaust system is required, as shown in Figure 4.6. This trimming system has a number of distinct advantages. It is inexpensive, safe to operate and the operation is not affected by ink composition or color. There are, however, some disadvantages. It is a dirty process and must take place in an area remote from the main production room. Only coarse trimming can be done as the smallest jet diameter is 0.5 mm. High value resistors can drift in value while trimming is taking place as the dry-air stream removes moisture from the component and cools it. Should this environment become too dry, static charges can be induced. Finally, the cut made opens up the natural resistor protective glaze so that resistor drift and noise performance degeneration occur.

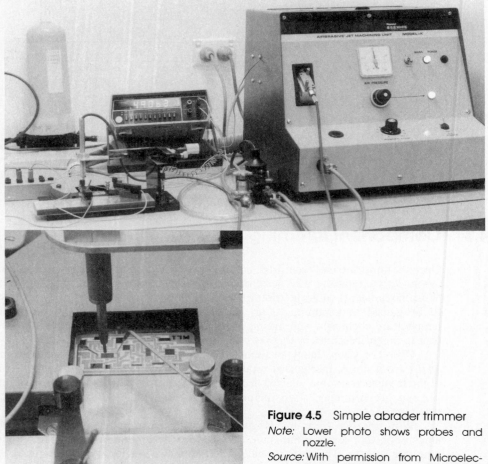

Figure 4.5 Simple abrader trimmer

Note: Lower photo shows probes and nozzle.

Source: With permission from Microelectronic Centre, South Australian Institute of Technology.

With laser trimming (Figures 4.7 and 4.8), a pulsed carbon dioxide (10.6 micron wavelength) or *Q* switched mode YAG (1.06 micron wavelength) laser of sufficient energy is used to vaporize part of the component. While the unit may have a peak power of up to 10 kW, with pulses of only 300 nanosec long, and at

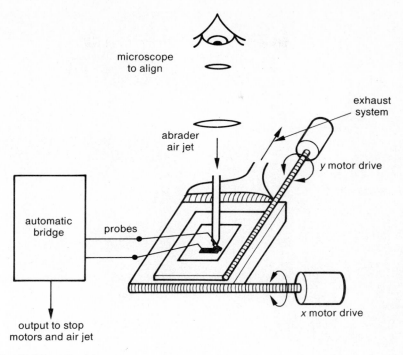

microscope
to align

exhaust
system

abrader
air jet

y motor drive

automatic
bridge

probes

x motor drive

output to stop
motors and air jet

Figure 4.6 Air abrasive trimmer

repetition pulse rates of 2–10 kHz, the average power is only a few watts. Again, a movable *xy* platform is used to mount the substrate with stepping motors driving the platform. Positioning accuracy of a few microns is possible and, with cuts of a few tens of microns wide, very precise trimming of components is possible.

Because a high power laser with a wavelength in the non-visible spectrum is used, extreme care must be taken to protect the operator. Interlocks on the trimming bay area, view via a remote TV camera, and computer control are all necessary precautions. There are typically four steps to the trimming cycle:

1. load the substrate;
2. measure components and compute trimming details;
3. trim the component;
4. unload position.

Like the abrader system, the laser trimming unit has advantages and disadvantages. Although it is very expensive and care must be taken to protect the eyes of the operator, the system is clean and easy to control by computer. It can achieve very precise, fine cuts allowing special trim cuts to eliminate component hot spots, while the heating during a trim reseals the glaze so that a resistor's long-term performance is not adversely affected. Unfortunately, the trim method is sensitive to paste colors, and there is for each paste type, an optimum evaporation

Figure 4.7   An *ESI* laser trimmer

Note: Lower photo shows the test head and interface circuit for dynamic trim.

Source: With permission from Philips Australia.

rate to minimize side effects such as resistor temperature coefficient, micro cracks in the substrate and accuracy of trim (the heating causes the component value to change during trim).

For any component, no matter which of the two methods of trim is used, there are several trim cuts that can be used. For resistors, these are illustrated in Figure 4.9(a) and (b). Note that in every case, resistors are trimmed up in value. With capacitors, the range of cuts is very restrictive as leakage paths can occur degrading the quality of the component. Unlike resistors, capacitors are trimmed down in value. Again the methods are illustrated in Figure 4.9.

Thus far it has been assumed that components are trimmed immediately after the final printing and firing. This is not always the case. The circuit can first be fully assembled thus allowing both passive and active trims. With passive trim, each component is simply trimmed to a desired set value, while with an active trim the component being trimmed is used to control some other circuit parameter. For example, a resistor may be trimed to zero out the offset of an operational amplifier.

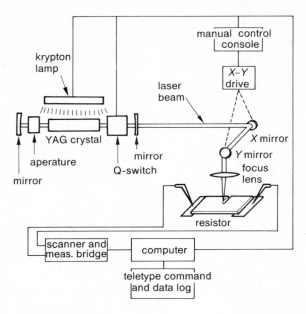

(a) *Laser trimmer*

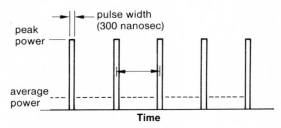

(b) *Typical pulse train*

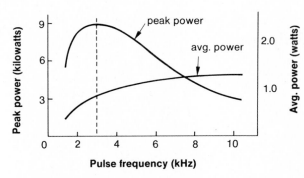

(c) *Power used*

Figure 4.8 Component parts and characteristics of a laser trimmer

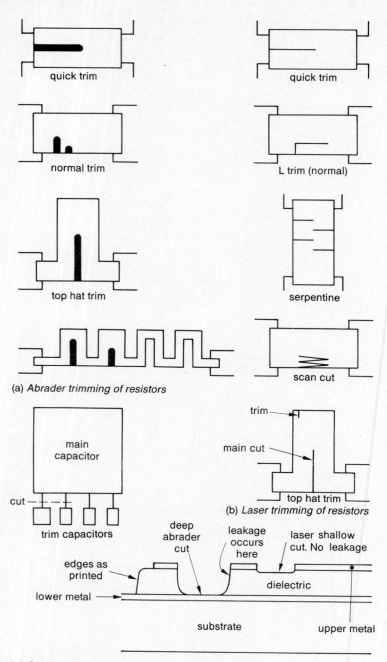

quick trim

normal trim

top hat trim

quick trim

L trim (normal)

serpentine

scan cut

(a) *Abrader trimming of resistors*

main capacitor

cut —

trim capacitors

trim

main cut

top hat trim

(b) *Laser trimming of resistors*

deep abrader cut

leakage occurs here

laser shallow cut. No leakage

edges as printed

dielectric

lower metal

substrate

upper metal

(c) *Capacitor trimming cuts*

Figure 4.9   Trimming of components

4.4 Exercises

1. Refer to Figure 4.6.
   (a) Why is the quick trim of resistors not recommended?
   (b) When is the top hat trim method used?
   (c) Why is the top hat method preferred to the serpentine? When may the serpentine cut be used?
   (d) Trimming of capacitors is not normally done. Why do you think this is so?

2. Thomas (1984) proposes a true three-terminal trim pot as shown in Figure 4.10.
   (a) Is it a practical circuit element?
   (b) Develop an electrical model for it.
   (c) For a unit made from sheet resistance R_s and aspect ratio L/W, what ranges of trim and re-trim would you expect?

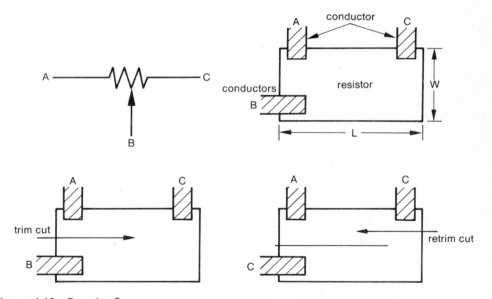

Figure 4.10 Exercise 2

4.5 References

Bradley, J. P. (1985), 'Copper Thick Film Nitrogen Atmosphere Furnace Design and Firing Process Considerations', *INSIDE ISHM*, vol. 12, no. 6, pp. 9–14.

Delott, C. R. (1985), 'Control of Furnace Atmosphere: Part 1—Furnace Adjustment', *Proc. 1985 International Symposium on Microelectronics*, 11–14 November, Anaheim, Cal., pp. 592–4.

Hamer, D. W. and J. V. Biggers (1973), *The Fundamentals of Thick-Film Hybrid Technology*, State of the Arts Inc., 1315 South Allen Street, State College, Pa., 16801.

Rao, M. K. and C. W. Loch (1985), 'Investigations on Infra-Red Fired Thick Film Resistor Layers', *Proc. 1985 International Symposium of Microelectronics*, 11–14 November, Anaheim, Cal., pp. 552–61.

Singh, A. (1976), 'Techniques of Adjusting Thin and Thick Film Resistors in Hybrid Microelectronic Circuits', *Microelectronics and Reliability*, vol. 15, pp. 123–9.

Smetana, W. (1985), 'Parameters Affecting Infrared Firing Process of Thick Film Resistors', *Proc. 1985 International Symposium on Microelectronics*, 11–14 November, Anaheim, Cal., pp. 574–82.

Thomas, R. (1984), 'The Trimmable Three Terminal Resistor: A True Trimpot for Laser Trimmed Circuits', *Proc. 1984 International Symposium on Microelectronics*, 17–19 September, Dallas, Tex., pp. 445–9.

5 Assembly, packaging and testing

5.1 The final steps

The printing, firing and trimming of substrates constitutes only the first half of the manufacturing process. There are many circuit elements that cannot be printed, or because of some undesirable characteristic it is preferable not to print them, so that components must be added in chip or discrete form. This is the assembly operation. Once this is completed, the circuit normally needs to be tested to ensure that it functions according to specifications. This test may include an active trim. When proven to be operating correctly, the unit then needs to be packaged to protect it both mechanically and from its working environment. A final test is then given to ensure correct operation, the unit type number stamped on it and it is then ready for marketing, burn in, or even life test if it is an early sample of a new product. In this chapter, we will examine these final steps in manufacture.

5.2 Chip assembly

As previously explained, the thick-film process does not allow the manufacture of active components, so all of these must be added at this point. There are, however, other elements, frequently passive components that must be mounted as well. For example, a printed capacitor or inductor may require too large an area, being therefore, either uneconomical to print or too large to be accommodated by the specified maximum substrate size. Precision resistors, capacitors with a wide frequency range performance, or inductors with high quality factors may be additional reasons for using discrete chip components.

Standard surface-mounting techniques are used to mount these components. Normal leaded components would require specially punched (when the substrate is green in the case of alumina), ultrasonically drilled or laser-cut holes, with these processes adding to the cost of the completed unit. The leadless, presoldered chip components are placed on their printed conductor pads, the pads first being screened with solder paste. The flux in the solder paste is sufficiently tacky to hold the component in place. A simple moving belt over a hot plate causes reflowing of the solder, the surface tension of the molten solder pulling the component into alignment with the pads should there have been a slight misalignment during placement. Other forms of heat used to reflow the solder include infrared, belt furnaces and vapor reflow.

Placement of the components can be undertaken manually but the normal method is to use pick-and-place machines. These robotic arms are intelligent, and after an operator guides the arm to place all components on the first substrate, it remembers the sequence of operations and repeats them for all the remaining substrates. A magnetic tape or disk with these placement instructions is generated so that the machine does not have to be retrained when subsequent batches of the same substrates are assembled. Figure 5.1 shows a placement machine.

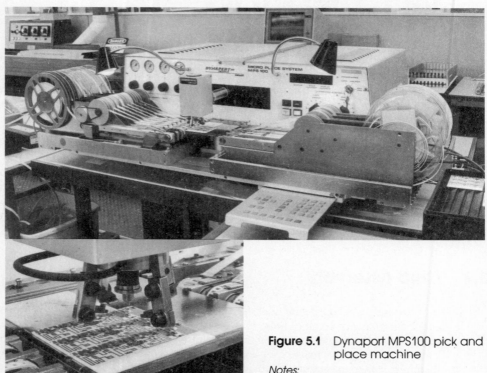

Figure 5.1   Dynaport MPS100 pick and place machine

Notes:
1. Components are fed in on tape reels.
2. Lower photo shows placement head.

Source: With permission from Philips Australia.

When reflow soldering methods are employed, care must be taken to ensure that manufacturers' recommendations are adhered to. Extract 5.1 gives recommendations of one manufacturer for its small outline discrete transistors. The maximum temperature allowed is 250°C and soldering must be executed within 10 seconds.

Extract 5.1   Soldering recommendations for small outline packaged transistors

The preferred technique for mounting micro miniature components on hybrid thick- and thin-film circuits is reflow soldering. The fernico-tags of the SOT-23 envelope are pretinned with a solder that melts at about 185°C. The best results are obtained when a similar solder is applied to the corresponding soldering areas on the substrate. This can be done by either dipping the substrate in a solder bath or by screen printing solder pastes. The component is put in place, a flux is added and the solder is reflowed by heating. For reliable connections the following should be kept in mind:

The maximum solder temperature and the proper flux are important. The flux must not affect the resistors and connectors, and its residue must be easy to remove. With the tags at the maximum permissible temperature (250°C) soldering must be done within 10 seconds. The maximum permissible rate of temperature change is 25°C/s.

The most economic procedure is a process in which all the components (SOT-23, chip capacitors, etc.) are soldered simultaneously. First having been fluxed, all components are positioned on the substrate. The slight adhesive force of the flux is sufficient to keep the components in place. The solder paste contains a flux and has therefore good inherent adhesive properties, which eases positioning of the components.

With the components in position, the substrate is heated to a point where the solder begins to flow. This can be done on a heater plate or on a conveyor belt running through an infrared tunnel. Depending on the equipment used and the size of the substrate, a full soldering cycle takes between 10 and 15 seconds, all solder being liquid only during the last 1 or 2 seconds.

The surface tension of the liquid solder tends to draw the tags of the transistor towards the center of the soldering area, which has a correcting effect on slight mispositionings. However, if the layout leaves something to be desired, the same effect can result in undesirable shifts, particularly if the soldering areas on substrate and component are not concentrically arranged. This problem is solved by using a standard contact pattern that leaves sufficient scope for the self-positioning effect.

Minimum required dimensions of metal connection pads on thick- and thin-film substrates.

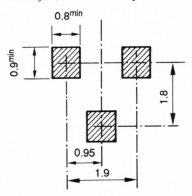

The solder having set and cooled off, the connections are visually inspected and, where necessary, put right with a soldering iron. Finally the remnants of the flux must be carefully removed.

It is also possible to solder the SOT-23 components with a miniature hand-held soldering iron, but the procedure has the following drawbacks and should, therefore, be restricted to laboratory use and/or incidental repairs on production circuits:

* It is expensive and time consuming.
* The semiconductors cannot be positioned accurately, and therefore the connecting tags may come into contact with the substrate and damage it.
* There is a great risk of breaking either the substrate or the connections inside the encapsulation; the encapsulation, too, may be damaged by the iron.

Source: Philips (various), *Electronic Components and Materials*, Philips Data Handbook (Red Series), Eindhoven, Holland

As an alternative to reflow soldering methods, conducting silver-loaded epoxy adhesive may be used to mount chip components. While the joint resistance (both electrical and thermal) can be several orders higher (although still low in value), the curing temperature of the epoxy is lower (typically $\leqslant 150°C$) than that required to reflow the solder. Use of the epoxy method is essential for components that cannot withstand the higher temperatures. Epoxy, however, takes a long time to cure.

The amount of epoxy used to form the bond is somewhat critical. Too little means a poor bond while an excess causes the epoxy to flow onto the top of the chip. This is fatal with silicon chips as the epoxy covers the bonding pads. Epoxy extrusion machines that measure out the correct amount for each die size are available.

With silicon chips, eutectic bonding is also possible if the pad onto which the chip is to be bonded is printed with an appropriate gold paste. Through heating, a silicon-gold eutectic is formed. The chip is usually vibrated (scrubbed) to ensure a good uniform bond. The substrate must be heated above the gold-silicon-eutectic point-temperature of 375°C, usually between 400 and 450°C, to ensure that there is an adequate amount of liquid phase present to form a satisfactory bond. An alternative approach is to use an intermediate tab. The molybdenum-gold tab is eutectically bonded to the silicon chip and then the tab can be tin-gold soldered at 300°C to the substrate.

5.2.1 Passive chip components

With the growing use of surface-mounting techniques for printed circuit boards, there is an increasing range of chip components available and steps are being taken to standardize sizes. Resistors generally come in one of two styles: cylindrical (METL) and rectangular, as shown in Figure 5.2(a). The resistor is either thick or thin film, using materials such as cermets, carbon, nickel, chromium and tantalum. The ends of resistors are normally presoldered; however, should epoxy mounting methods be used then components can be purchased that are not pretinned.

Capacitors are normally rectangular in shape, having longer dimensions as the capacitor value increases. As with leaded capacitors, polyester, ceramic, tantalum and other dielectric types are available.

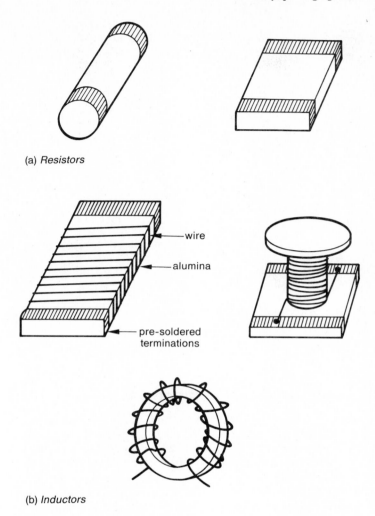

(a) *Resistors*

wire

alumina

pre-soldered
terminations

(b) *Inductors*

Figure 5.2 Common styles for chip resistors and inductors

Chip inductors are, in general, of non-standard construction and range from ceramic former 'air core' types to ferrite toroids. More recently, special ferrite bobbin-types are becoming readily available. The toroid inductors must be soldered in by hand.

The majority of the passive chip components are available in sprocketed blister tape reels ready for automatic placement. The blister tape is a strip of plastic ranging from 8–24 mm in width, that has small depressions formed along its length by heat to take the components. A thin plastic strip seals in the components.

Figure 5.3 shows a variety of surface-mount passive components.

Figure 5.3 Assortment of surface mount passive components including resistors, capacitors, and inductor

Source: With permission from Philips Australia

5.2.2 Semiconductor components

Active devices are available both in die form and in a variety of different surface-mounting packages. These packages may be unleaded as are the JEDEC chip carrier styles or leaded such as the small outline gull leads or the J lead. These styles are illustrated in Figure 5.4. The spacing of the package leads or pads is normally 50 mil but pads can be on 40, 25 or even 20 mil spacing. Japanese packages tend not to keep to a common standard, but vary the spacing with the total lead count of a package. Figure 5.5 shows a range of active surface-mount component types.

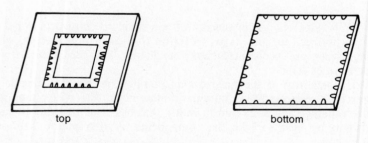

top   bottom

(a) *JEDEC leadless ceramic chip carrier*

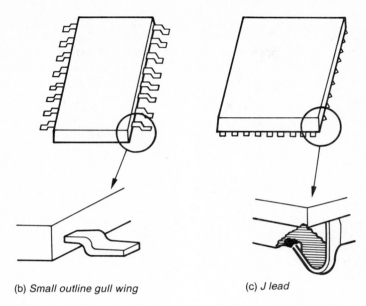

(b) *Small outline gull wing*   (c) *J lead*

Figure 5.4   Surface-mount package type

Figure 5.5   Selection of surface mount semi-conductor components including transistors and integrated circuits

Source: With permission from Philips Australia.

All of these devices come either in blister tape reels (particularly packages with small lead counts) or in plastic tubes. The plastic normally has a transparent conductive coating over it to ensure that there is no electrostatic charge build-up causing damage to the components contained inside.

Other packaged mounting styles do exist and include the ceramic flip chip package, beam lead and tape automatic bonding type (TAB). This latter method is growing in use in some countries, particularly where very large volumes of a product are being produced. There are several versions but they all depend on having an etched foil frame to achieve the mechanical transformation from the chip pad spacing (say 250 microns) to the final spacing where interconnection to the outside world is made (say 50 mil). These lead frames, with the chips mounted on them, are on a sprocketed polyimide strip. The frames and chips are punched off the tape before soldering into place on a substrate.

Where die and bonding methods are employed, the die must first be correctly positioned (including orientation) and fixed to the substrate using either the epoxy or eutectic methods already discussed. Wire bonding is then made between the die pads and the thick-film conductors. The conductor paste selected must be satisfactory for the type of wire bonding to be used.

Three bonding methods are in use:

1. thermo compression;
2. ultrasonic;
3. thermosonic.

There are a variety of thermo compression bonding approaches including nail head, ball and wedge. Often only gold wire of 20 (0.8 mil) to 62.5 microns (2.5 mil) is used, the normal being 25 microns (1 mil). Larger sizes are used for the higher currents of power devices. An alternative that can improve reliability is to use the standard wire size, but do multiple wire bonds in parallel. Figure 5.6(a) illustrates the stitch bonding process. The substrate is heated to 300°–350°C.

The gold wire is fed through a heated ceramic capillary and pressed with a force of about 25 grams on to the die aluminum pad. A thermo compression bond is formed. The capillary moves, taking the wire with it, to the thick-film paste and repeats the compression process. The capillary then moves vertically, allowing a pair of cutters to cut the wire ready for the commencement of the next bond. The bonding is done in an atmosphere of nitrogen to prevent oxidization.

If a gold bond wire is used and the temperature of the substrate is too high (>400°C) then intermetallic compounds between the gold and aluminum form. They have a brown to purple color and are very brittle and subject to fracture, causing circuit failure. This assembly problem is called 'purple plague'. Aluminum bond wires to aluminum pads do not have this problem. However if the package has gold fingers then the 'plague' can still occur.

With ultrasonic bonding the energy is supplied electronically from a 40 kHz generator through a magnetostrictive transducer. Pressure and the ultrasonic vibration cause plastic flow of the materials at normal ambient temperatures (Figure 5.6(b)). Gold or aluminum wire can be used.

The final method, thermosonic bonding, is a combination of the previous two processes. The substrate is heated to a temperature in the range 150°–300°C and

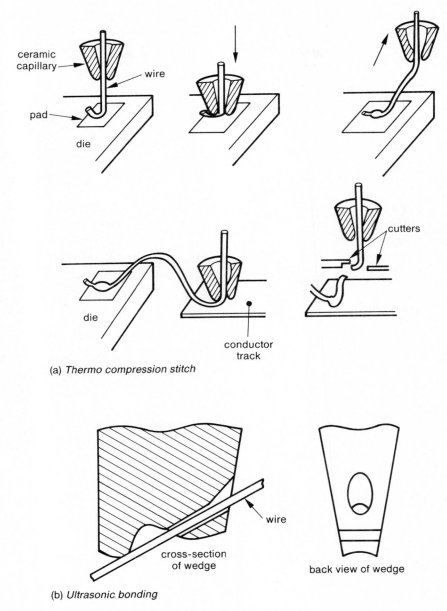

ceramic capillary

wire

pad

die

die

conductor track

cutters

(a) *Thermo compression stitch*

wire

cross-section of wedge

back view of wedge

(b) *Ultrasonic bonding*

Figure 5.6   Wire bonding methods

the bond is made ultrasonically. This process is more tolerant to material variations.

While each of these processes seems complex, they are normally carried out on a semi to fully automatic bonder. In the latter case, the equipment is like the pick-and-place machines in that the operator teaches the machine by performing the full bonding of a die once, and thereafter the machine knows. All that the operator may have to do is to align the machine to the first pad. Figure 5.7 shows a typical wire bonding machine.

Figure 5.7 K and S automatic wire bonder

Note: Insert shows the bond tip in operation.
Source: With permission from Philips Australia.

5.3 Packaging

(See Harper, 1970; Sinnadurai, 1985.)

The protection given to a finished thick-film module depends very much on the type of product quality required. Normally, three grades are available. In the order of increasing requirements and, therefore, cost, they are consumer, industrial and military. Table 5.1 shows that the maximum temperature of use is set by the packaging techniques. As the table suggests, the packaging methods can be subdivided into four types: coated, molded, cast and hermetic seal. Naturally, the very simplest case is where no chip components are required and a simple glass paste can be screen-printed over the entire substrate. This, however, is not being considered as a separate packaging operation.

Package used for product	*Maximum recommended temperature product used, °C*
Conformal coating	150
Hermetic solder seal	150
Molded	150+
Cast	200
Hermetic welded or reflow glass	250+

Table 5.1 Maximum recommended temperature of operation using various packaging techniques

There are two distinct coatings: fluid and powder. With the fluid, the substrate is dipped into it, the excess fluid is allowed to run off and then it is dried at an elevated temperature of 100°C. With the powder, the substrate must also be coated, often by preheating the substrate and dipping it into the powder. The unit is then heated to a higher temperature (150°C), allowing the coating to cure. Coating materials may be epoxy, phenolic, diallyl phthalate or urethane types.

Molding resins can be of similar materials to the coatings given above. In the early days, some of these materials proved troublesome in that they reacted with pastes, causing resistors to increase slowly in value, and eventually the circuits failed. This problem has mainly been resolved, unless one is looking for the ultimate in reliability. Another difficulty is the high dielectric constants of some materials so that all stray capacities are scaled. For example, a dielectric constant of 5 is not uncommon. Casting resins can also be epoxy, polyester or phenolic types and, therefore, have similar properties. Silicons are also used. Another difficulty with molding and casting is the difference in thermal coefficients of expansion between the materials used and an alumina substrate. For example, the coefficient of thermal expansion for alumina is 6.8×10^{-6} per °C while for an epoxy 50×10^{-6} per °C. Consequently, glass, mica and other filler types are added to the epoxy to help compensate for this large difference in coefficient.

Yet another difficulty with the use of epoxies and resins for packaging is that they de-gas when heated, with these gases eventually causing degradation and failure of the circuit. The final problem to be mentioned is the ingress of water vapor that these methods of packaging allow. With a list of problems so long, one may ask why use these methods. The answer is that, in spite of these degrading effects, the life of the product is still many years and the packaging costs involved to improve the life are normally not warranted. Only in the case where the ultimate reliability is required is the hermetic type package employed. They are normally of ceramic construction with gold-plated leads. The thick-film unit is placed inside the self-supporting packages and wires are bonded from the substrate to the package internal pads. A gold-plated metal lid is fixed on top by soldering, welding or using a low temperature melting glass seal.

Prior to encapsulating, when using coatings, casting or molding resins, all bonded dies must be completely covered with a flexible material such as a silicon sealant to protect the bonds from the forces developed during curing of the encapsulant. If this is not done, the shrinkage that occurs can destroy the wire bonds. Figure 5.8 shows a variety of ways thick-film circuits may be packaged.

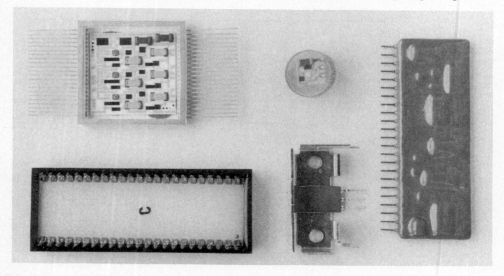

Figure 5.8   Thick-film circuits can be packaged in a variety of ways depending on cost and customer needs
Source: With permission from Philips Australia.

5.4   Testing

Electrical testing of the finished unit is carried out in the normal manner for any electronic product. The specification will include a functional test that may need to be carried out at the extremes of supply voltage tolerances and over a specified temperature range. Depending upon the customer's needs, a whole range of environmental tests may have to be performed on early samples. Drop, vibration, impact, humidity and mold growth are examples of the requirements for the tests taken from various standards documents including MIL specifications. In some cases, the required product reliability may mean that burn-in of units must occur in order to take the units through the infant mortality portion of their failure rate bathtub curve.

5.5 References

Harper, C. A. (ed.), (1970), *Handbook of Materials and Processes for Electronics*, McGraw-Hill, New York.

Philips (various), *Electronic Components and Materials*, Philips Data Handbook (Red Series), Eindhoven, Holland.

Sinnadurai, F. N. (1985) *Handbook of Microelectronics Packaging and Interconnection Technologies*, Electrochemical Publication, Ayre, Scotland.

6 Cleanliness and safety

6.1 Introduction

The ultimate reliability of a product depends on many factors including the inbuilt design safety factors, numbers of joints and cleanliness (Cabelka and Archer, 1985) of the manufacturing process. This latter factor includes the cleanliness of raw materials such as substrates, the quality of chemical used, the purity of the water, the garments the operators wear and the cleanliness of the surroundings in which the unit is made. With the manufacturing of integrated circuits where dimensions can be submicron, the attention to cleanliness has reached the point where semiconductor foundries are cleaner than operating theaters in hospitals. Fortunately, with thick film, the minimum dimensions are at least an order greater so that the ultimate in cleanliness is not essential in order to make reliable thick-film hybrids. That is not to say that one can ignore cleanliness. Every step that can be introduced to improve the cleanliness of the process will improve product quality. Naturally cleanliness is a costly business and each step introduced has to be looked at to see if the market being served requires and is prepared to pay for the increased product quality.

Cleanliness comes hand-in-hand with safety. Many of the chemicals used to ensure clean devices are toxic, volatile and have low ignition energy levels. Consequently, adequate safety standards must be built into any operation. We will briefly examine each topic.

6.2 Clean rooms

Whether or not a clean room is required for the manufacture of the thick-film circuits depends upon a number of factors. The following two will be considered here:

1. what market is being aimed at;
2. what process step is being used.

To establish a production line to manufacture to MIL standards, a good clean room is essential for all aspects of production. Various clean room standards documents are available, giving three classifications: 3500 (100 000), 350 (10 000) and 3.5 (100), where the figure indicates the number of particles of 0.5 micron-size or larger per liter (per cubic foot). Figure 6.1 gives the allowable particle size distribution (Australian Standards Documents).

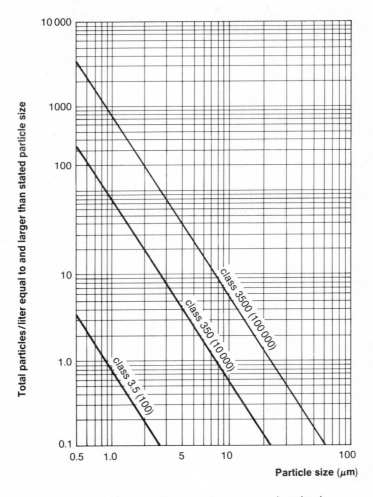

Figure 6.1 Particle size distribution for the three clean room standards classifications

Temperature and humidity limits must also be controlled. For example, RCA made its main area class 350 (Davis, 1986). The measurement of the number of particles in a clean room is an interesting exercise and is done using a light-scattering monitor. The unit draws in a known volume of air and, in so doing, the air with the particles passes through a beam of monochromatic light. Light reflected by the particles is sensed by a photocell and the intensity or count received is read from a counter connected to the photocell. The air can be drawn in through filters of various sizes so that a histogram of count versus particle size can be determined.

There are two basic approaches to clean conditions. The first is to set up laminar flow conditions, either across a room or vertically with a perforated wall or floor being the exit, as shown in Figures 6.2(a) and 6.3. In most cases, this is not required for thick-film work. A simple clean room is to have filtered clean air

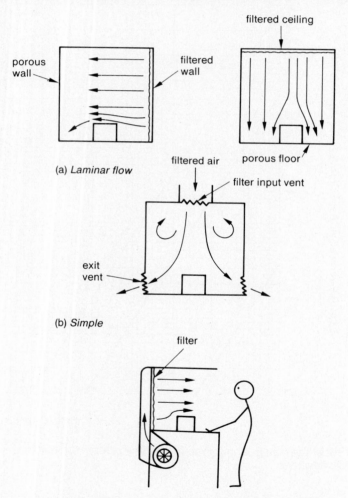

(a) *Laminar flow*

(b) *Simple*

(c) *A laminar flow bench (horizontal–vertical also available)*

Figure 6.2   Clean room methods

coming from a ceiling input vent, having the final filter at the vent, with exit vents at floor level. A positive pressure ensures that air does not flow back into the room through the exit vents. This is illustrated in Figure 6.2(b). Eddy currents do exist and they can hold in suspension light particles; however, most heavy particles introduced by workers' footwear will remain at floor level. Filters used for this room are typically 5 microns in size and the 3500 class can easily be achieved. Should some processes require a class better than this, then laminar flow benches, as illustrated in Figures 6.2(c) and 6.4, can be introduced into these processing areas. Class 3.5 is easily achieved.

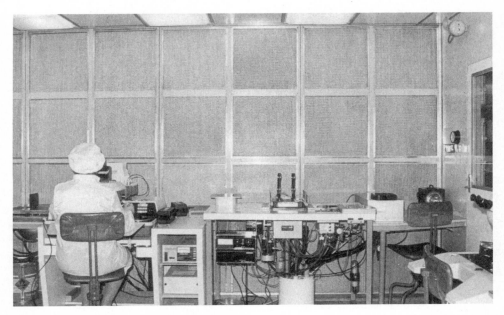

Figure 6.3 Horizontal laminar clear room
Note: Inlet filters are in the distant wall.
Source: With permission from Philips Australia.

For many commercial and industrial applications, normal office air-conditioning is adequate for most processing steps.

Perhaps the greatest source of contamination of production clean rooms is the operator. Human hair is typically 30 to 100 microns in diameter, while dandruff (dead skin cells) and other particles shed by people range from less than 0.5 to over 500 microns in size. Table 6.1 indicates typical quantities of these particles shed every minute. To contain these particles, some form of garment should be worn. Special garments are available that are lint free and are therefore preferred (Australian Standards Documents).

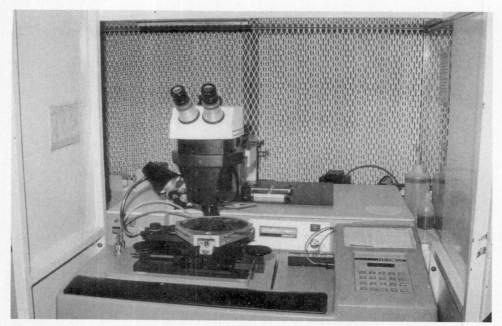

Figure 6.4   Laminar flow bench to ensure clean conditions at the work position
Source: With permission from Philips Australia.

Activity	Typical quantity of particles shed by an adult per minute
Still, no movement	10^5
Sitting with slight head and hand movement	5×10^5
Sitting with increased movement	10^6
Rising from sitting to standing	2.5×10^6
Average walking speed	7.5×10^6

Table 6.1   Quantities of particles shed by humans

No matter whether normal office air-conditioning or a proper clean room is used, it is important that good housekeeping procedures be kept. There are four essential elements:

1. Instigate adequate yet sufficient cleaning. Install a central vacuum-cleaning system with floor-ducted pipes and a power unit outside the room. Make sure liquid cleaners are used and not powders.
2. Place shoe brushes and sticky dust collecting mats (Tak Mats) at an entrance to remove dirt from shoes. If better control is required then shoe covers can be used.

3. Keep control of all waste material, removing all possible contaminants.
4. Supply each worker with an appropriate garment to wear. Minimize their movement.

6.3   Quality materials

To achieve consistent, repeatable results with high reliability, it is essential that all processing steps be precisely defined and be repeatable for each product run. This means it is necessary to employ high quality materials and chemicals. Electronic grade chemicals are the preferred grade.

Substrates, for example, should be ultrasonically cleaned before printing. The cleaning and degreasing of the substrate can be undertaken in stages, with the final wash being in deionized (DI) water of purity greater than 1 Mohm.

Table 6.2 gives the order of the quality of cleaning chemicals measured in terms of residual solvents on a substrate after manufacture and prior to packaging (Sinnadurai, 1985).

Cleaning material	*Resistivity of residual solvents*
Detergent	lowest (worst)
Acetone	
Trichloroethylene	
Isopropyl alcohol	
Deionized water	highest (best)

Table 6.2   Resistivity of residual solvents

At all times, the ultimate in cleanliness should be the goal. For example, screens should be carefully scrubbed to ensure that there are no residual pastes or particles blocking mesh openings; before packaging, all solder fluxes should be cleaned off units, etc. The omission of any one of these simple steps can mean a low yield or poor product.

6.4   Safety

The majority of chemicals used in normal thick-film processing are solvents. No highly acidic, alkaline or corrosive chemical is employed, such as ferric chloride in the printed wiring industry or hydrofluoric acid in integrated circuit fabrication. Yet this does not mean there are no dangers arising from the solvent chemicals used (Scott, 1967; Weeks, 1972). Normally solvents should be used in small volumes in exhausted areas. Hydrocarbons are nontoxic (benzene is a serious exception with toluene and xylene to a lesser extent), but present a flammability hazard.

Alcohols are of relatively low toxicity yet are highly inflammable, while halogenated solvents like trichloroethylene present a toxic hazard and are not recommended. Overexposure to the vapor results in fainting and intoxication. Damage to the eyes and an upset of the nervous system can occur. Direct contact with the skin causes redness, dryness and cracking. As a precaution, all solvents should be treated with care.

Another difficulty with solvents is that many plastics are soluble in them. Consequently, care must be taken to ensure that the solvents are kept in bottles or containers of the correct type (Weeks, 1972). Finally, many solvents require little energy to ignite them. Table 6.3 lists several illustrative materials and the energy required to ignite them. With the low energy ones, even an electrostatic discharge can be sufficient to ignite them. To prevent this from happening, as well as protecting semiconductor devices, antistatic benches, equipment and straps should be used. Figure 6.5 shows an antistatic workstation.

Material	*Explosive range (% concentration by volume)*	*Minimum ignition energy (joules)*
Acetone	2.6–12.8	6×10^{-4}
Benzene	1.4– 7.1	5×10^{-4}
Ethyl alcohol	3.3–19.0	6.5×10^{-4}
Methyl alcohol	6.7–36.0	5×10^{-4}
Hydrogen	4.0–75.0	2×10^{-5}

Table 6.3 Explosive range of various materials

6.5 References

Australian Standards Documents: AS 1386 Clean Rooms and Work Stations. AS 1387 Code for Clean Rooms and Work Stations. AS 1807 Methods to Test Clean Rooms and Accessories. AS 2013.4 Clean Room Garments.

Cabelka, T. D. and Archer, W. L. (1985), 'Cleaning: What Really Counts', *Proc. 1985 International Symposium on Microelectronics*, 11–14 November, Anaheim, Cal., pp. 520–8.

Davis, M. (1986), 'Surface Mount Technology Experience: Problems and Solutions', *Microelectronics Journal*, vol. 17, no. 2, pp. 33–6.

Scott, A. M. (1967), 'Health Hazards in the Production of Printed Wiring', *Trans. Inst. of Metal Finishings*, vol. 45, pp. 102–6.

Sinnadurai, F. N. (1985), *Handbook of Microelectronics Packaging and Interconnection Technologies*, Electrochemical Publications Ltd, Ayre, Scotland.

Weeks, R. D. (1972), 'Solvents and Their Effects on Capacitors', *Electronic Components*, 10 March, pp. 231–4.

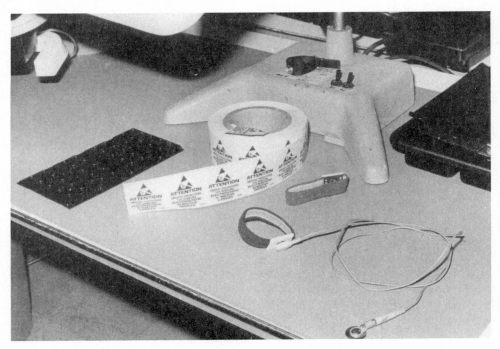

Figure 6.5 Anti-static work station showing wrist strap and anti-static mat
Note: The work station is used for packaging and labeling products
Source: With permission from Philips Australia.

7 Basic design concepts

7.1 Process limitations

Setting up a manufacturing facility is one thing, but to use it successfully to produce a range of working circuits is another. Many factors must be considered, particularly the limitations of the manufacturing facility. These limitations include the range and quality of component types that can be produced, the resolution of the process in terms of line width and spacing, and any variations in component characteristics as they are scaled in size. We will consider these factors in turn and then compile a set of layout rules that will allow circuits to be designed.

7.2 Component types

The components that the thick-film process is best at producing are conductors and resistors. Of these two, the thick-film process probably produces better resistors than conductors as most resistor pastes come in decade step sheet resistances, so that there is always a paste to match the resistance value required, giving a resistance of near minimum area. Conductor pastes tend to have a higher resistance than copper wire or track on a printed circuit board. However, both are available. Other components such as large capacitors, inductors and semiconductor devices must be added in discrete form—an extra step. Thus the thrust of true thick-film circuit design is to maximize the component types that the process is good at, namely, resistors and conductors. This is different from, say, integrated circuit design where the basic element is a transistor and therefore every effort is made to replace resistors by transistors (active loads, etc.). Compare the design of an amplifier as given in Figure 7.1.

The design of circuits employing mainly resistors is, therefore, not unlike the design of discrete component circuitry. There is, however, a significant advantage in that the resistor's value and size are under the designer's control. There is no need to stick to the preferred tolerance range. Resistors can also be trimmed in value and left to that value, so trim potentiometer numbers can sometimes be reduced.

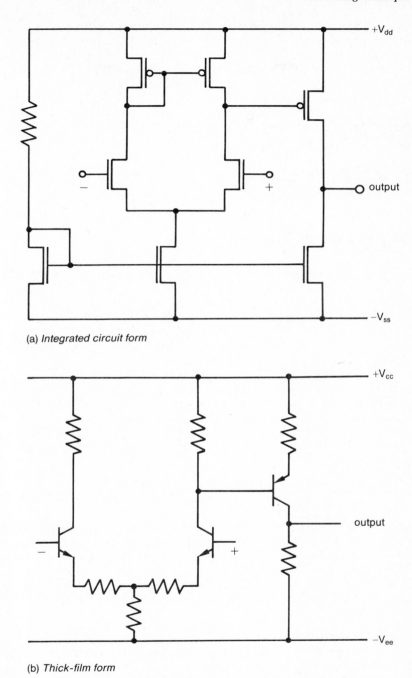

(a) *Integrated circuit form*

(b) *Thick-film form*

Figure 7.1   Different design approaches to produce an amplifier

Using conductors as the major circuit component may come as a surprise to some, but the method is common in UHF/microwave applications (e.g. strip-line techniques used on printed wiring boards). Here, with thick-film microstrip, conductors of various length/width ratios can be made to look resistive, capacitive or inductive. More of this will be given in the next chapter.

An alternative use of conductors as a major circuit component is the interconnection of VLSI chips. While this may seem obvious, it is a very common application of thick-film circuits. A good example of this is the single in-line package (SIP), where memory chips are first assembled onto the thick-film substrate to allow stacking horizontally as well as vertically to achieve a much higher packing density.

Thus the thrust in thick-film circuit design is to employ circuit techniques that maximize the number of resistors and conductors that are used.

7.3   Printed width and spacing

Two factors that determine how small a component may be printed is the minimum track that can be printed and the minimum spacing that can be achieved between two printings. Naturally, this depends on the screen size employed, finer meshes (higher number) allowing smaller dimensions. With a standard 200 mesh screen, 0.5 mm (20 mil) track and spacing can be readily achieved, while 320 mesh allows 0.25 mm (10 mil). With care even 150 micron can be achieved, but it is usual to change to an etched metal-foil screen.

Unfortunately, thick-film circuits are multilayered so that while it may be possible to achieve these minimum dimensions repeatedly as a first printing on a substrate, such may not be the case with later printings. This has two consequences. First, if a component size is critical, then try and print it as early as possible and onto the substrate. Second, the apparent sheet resistance (and other paste parameters like dielectric constant) changes with component size. For example:

1. excessively short resistors tend to be thinner since not very much ink can be squeezed into the narrow gap between the two conductor tracks, one at either end to make contact (Figure 7.2(a));
2. moderately sized resistors tend to be thicker since the screen cannot be forced between the conductors and so tends to ride over them, resulting in a large distance between the screen and the substrate, consequently filling the gap with ink;
3. with long resistors, that is, greater than 2 mm (50 mil), the screen is forced between the two conductors and so an even thickness occurs over the whole length.

These effects are shown in Figure 7.2(b).

It is interesting to note that a reduction in sheet resistance is of no real consequence if the resistor is to be trimmed. However, an increase in sheet resistance is catastrophic, as the trimming process can only trim resistors up in value as it achieves trimming by removing paste.

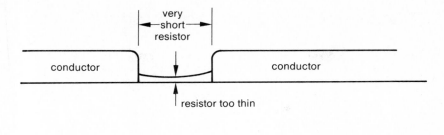

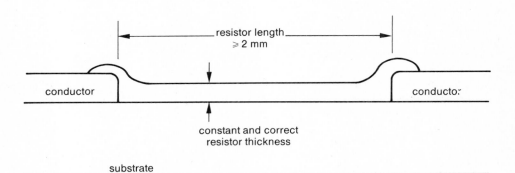

(a) *Effect on paste thickness*

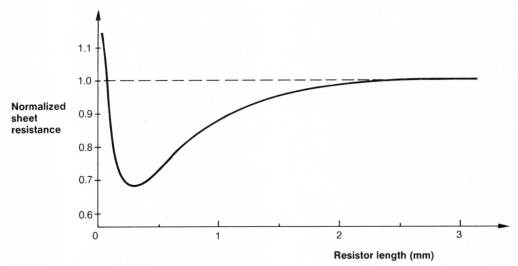

(b) *Effect on sheet resistance*

Figure 7.2 Effect on resistor length

7.4 Scaling components and aspect ratios

Aspect ratio and absolute size of a component are two important parameters. Again, considering a resistor, the aspect ratio determines the actual resistance while the absolute dimensions determine the total area occupied, hence dissipation allowed and packing density. Where dissipation is not a problem, then the smallest dimension of the resistor is normally made the minimum dimension recommended for the process, say 1 mm. Thus a long resistor would have a 1 mm width and a wide resistor a 1 mm length. In this way, maximum packing density is achieved. This approach does have a strong bearing on the useful range of aspect ratios that can be used for any resistor paste.

Consider Figure 7.3 (Mathews, 1973; Milson, 1973), which is a typical plot of normalized sheet resistance value against aspect ratio where the smallest dimension of the resistor is kept at the minimum dimension allowed by the process. At very small and for some pastes at large aspect ratios, the sheet resistance departs significantly from the maker's value. Reasons for this are as follows: Where the resistor paste abuts the conductor paste, there is an interaction during firing so that some of the conductor flows into the resistor paste reducing the sheet resistance at the points of abutment. With small aspect ratio resistors, this region is a major portion of the resistor length so that the net effect is that the resistance is low in value. This is called the 'end effect' and its contribution to lowering the sheet resistance can be calculated and allowed for in a stable process. As a rule, this is not done as a resistor can always be trimmed up in value.

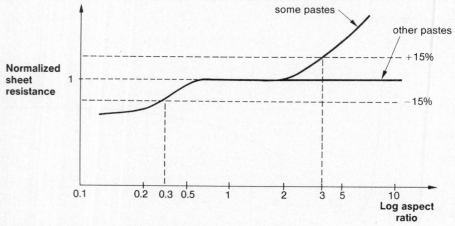

Figure 7.3 Plot of sheet resistance change versus aspect ratio

For very long resistors, there is often a thinning of the width so that the resistor value increases. Not all pastes show the same degree of increase in sheet resistance. Further, the graph over its whole range does vary slightly when the resistor is perpendicular to the squeegee direction of motion as opposed to being in the same direction.

Examining Figure 7.3 again shows that if a tolerance of about ± 15 percent on the sheet resistance is acceptable, then aspect ratios of $\frac{1}{3}$–3 can be used. This 9 to 1 range in resistance value for a paste fits in nicely with pastes being available in decade sheet resistance steps. Aspect ratios from $\frac{1}{5}$–5 are acceptable if some degradation in printing tolerance is allowable, as this could mean in some instances the saving of a screen and printing of an additonal resistor paste. It should be noted that resistors outside the $\frac{1}{5}$–5 aspect ratio start to take up excessive substrate area and a change to a more appropriate paste sheet resistance is recommended.

7.5   Quality of a component

The quality of the resultant components is determined by the manufacturing process and the paste selected. Assuming a clean, stable process, any poor quality component is either due to incorrect paste selection or the quality required exceeds that possible from current thick-film pastes. An added chip may be the only solution. The question still arises as to how good thick-film components are. For example, for a resistor paste, what are typical temperature coefficients, voltage coefficients, noise generated and aging characteristics? Many results have been published on this topic (Sinnadurai et al., 1980; Ringo et al., 1976; Janoska, 1983; Gosselin et al., 1975; Microelectronics Centre SAIT). The following is a summary for cermet pastes on ceramic substrates, although there are always pastes that are exceptions to any rule and, therefore, any paste a designer selects must be checked out.

7.5.1   Temperature coefficient of resistance

The temperature coefficient of resistance (TCR) for most resistor pastes is typically ± 200 ppm/°C at ambient temperature, but can be as low as ± 50. There are many factors that influence the TCR, including paste sheet resistance, cofired or not, peak firing temperature and resistor dimensions. Figure 7.4 shows the effect of peak firing temperature.

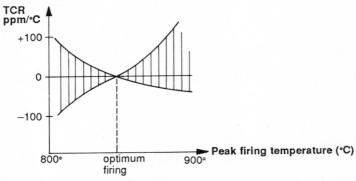

Figure 7.4   Effect of peak firing temperature on temperature coefficient of resistance (TCR)

When the length of a resistor becomes small, say less than 1 mm, the coefficient tends to decrease in value with some pastes. Presumably this is due to the interaction with the conductor paste and no doubt will depend on conductor paste type. Cofiring of resistor and conductor pastes also tends to reduce the temperature coefficient of resistance (Microelectronics Centre SAIT). By and large, the TCR occurs because of the conduction mechanism and as a second order effect of the difference in thermal coefficient of expansion between the paste and substrate.

The bulk resistivity of the paste with time, $\rho(T)$, can be expressed as (Sinnadurai, 1980):

$$\rho(T) \,=\, K\, T^{\frac{1}{2}}\, e^{\left(\frac{T}{T_o}\right)^{\frac{1}{4}}} \tag{7.1}$$

where:

T is the temperature in $^\circ K$
K is a proportionality constant
$To \,=\, \dfrac{16\alpha^3}{k\, No}$
k is Boltzman's constant
No is the density of the conductive grains per unit volume and per unit energy
α is a parameter correlated to the grain size and glass characteristic

Figure 7.5 shows typical characteristics of a resistor with temperature.

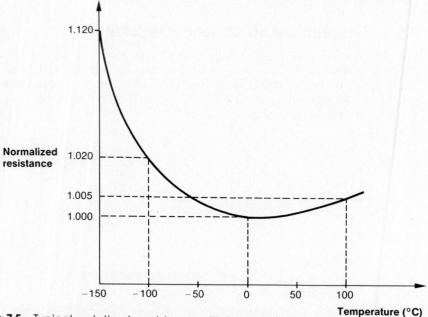

Figure 7.5   Typical variation in resistance with temperature

7.5.2 Voltage coefficient of resistance

The voltage coefficient of resistance for a modern paste has a typical value of 20 ppm/V/cm, the value increasing rapidly with some pastes for short resistors (<1 mm). It is usually only important for high value sheet resistance pastes ($\geqslant 100$ kohm per square).

7.5.3 Piezo-resistance effect

The resistance of the paste changes with flexing of the substrate. The resistance change is linear with strain, reversible, decreasing in compression and increasing in tension. Little hysteresis effect is seen. A typical value of percentage change in resistance per unit strain is 1000 (Janoska, 1983).

7.5.4 Noise of resistors

Being a cermet, this is a mixture of metal and metal oxide, the pastes show noise that is current or voltage dependent.

Thus,

$$\frac{(\Delta i)^2}{(I)} = \frac{(\Delta v)^2}{(V)} = Kq\mu \frac{R}{L^2} \frac{\Delta f}{f} \qquad (7.2)$$

where:

Δi and Δv are the noise current or voltage
I and V are the applied DC current or voltage
K is the proportionality constant
q is the electron charge
μ is the effective charge mobility
R is the resistor value
L is the resistor length
Δf is the noise bandwidth
f is the center frequency of the noise bandwidth

Note it is a $1/f$ noise. Fortunately, the noise level generated is low so that thick-film resistors have good noise characteristics. An interesting property is that the noise depends on the geometry of the resistor as well as the resistor value. For example, trimmed top hat resistors give less noise than trimmed rectangular resistors of the same resistance. Equation 7.2 indicates that the noise is inversely proportional to the volume of the resistor.

Thermal noise and burst noise also occur in a thick-film resistor (Chen and Cottle, 1986).

7.5.5 Aging of resistors

The aging characteristics of resistors vary considerably with paste type, whether or not it is encapsulated and the conditions under which aging is occurring. Resistors all increase their values with time and an increase in humidity level speeds up the process. Some encapsulants still degrade the performance of resistors with age while others give a marked improvement (Microelectronics Centre SAIT). Sinnadurai et al., (1980) report that if the Arrhenius relationship holds under thermal aging:

$$t = \alpha t_0 e^{\frac{Ea}{kT}} \tag{7.3}$$

where:

t is time
T is temperature $^\circ$K
α is a proportionality constant
k is Boltzman's constant

then the activation energies (Ea) lie in the range 0.5–1.5 eV; while if damp heat aging obeys the relationship:

$$t = \beta t_0 e^{C(RH)^2} \tag{7.4}$$

where:

RH is the relative humidity
C is a constant approximately 10^{-4}
β is a proportionality constant.

7.5.6 Properties of other component types

While the discussion has been restricted in the main to resistors, similar comments could be made about other components. Capacitor dielectric and hence capacitors show temperature effect, have a voltage coefficient and may display hysteresis effects with frequency.

One major difficulty with crystallizing dielectric pastes is the drastic changes they introduce to resistors; when resistors are printed on them sheet resistance can change by a factor of 3 up to as high as 50 (Janoska, 1983; Pitt and Gledhill, 1984). At present, a major effort is being made to understand why this change occurs and to correct it by designing new high temperature dielectric pastes with ceramic crystalline fillers that are more suitable for multilayer work.

7.5.7 Print or use a chip component

Should printed components not be able to give the desired properties then the decision whether or not to print the component or mount it in chip form does not exist. This is frequently the case with capacitors. In many instances a choice is available, the deciding factor being the ultimate cost. Figure 7.6 shows three factors that must be taken into consideration—size of the production run, number of components to be used and substrate area.

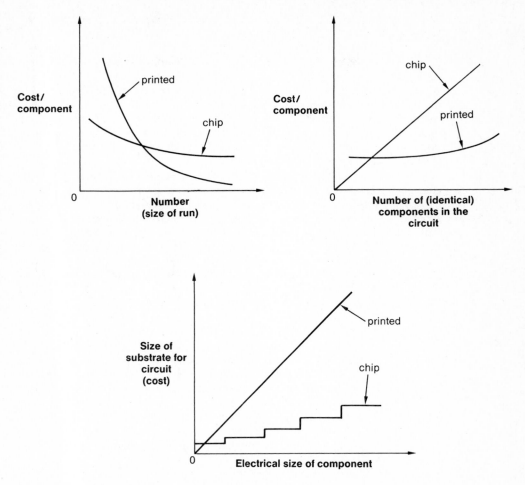

Figure 7.6 Factors that need to be considered when deciding whether or not to use chip component

7.6　Typical layout rules

Because most manufacturers of thick film employ similar equipment, often using identical pastes and frequently having to second source each other, the process specifications and rules used to lay out a circuit are nearly identical. Consequently, with care it is possible to generate a set of basic portable layout rules which ensure that, at worst, with minor changes (e.g. alignment marks) it is possible to have the circuit processed by any thick-film hybrid manufacturer. The following is such a set of rules, given here in some detail, while Appendix B gives a simple summary for convenience:

1. Artwork when produced manually is to be drawn at ×10 final size on a stable base material.
2. All outside conductor edges should be kept 0.5 mm (20 mil) minimum inside the perimeter of the substrate.
3. Normally external lead pads should be 1.5 × 2 mm (60 × 80 mil), the 1.5 mm (60 mil) running parallel to the substrate edge. It is normal to place them on 2.54 mm (100 mil) centers either down one side (SIP) or two parallel sides (DIP) of the substrate. See Figure 7.7(a).
4. Conductor path lengths should be kept as short as possible. Minimum width and spacing is 0.4 mm (16 mil).
5. Crossovers require extra printings of insulator and conductor and should be avoided. Crossover pastes to extend beyond conductors by 0.4 mm (16 mil).
6. Pad areas for mounting semiconductor devices that need bonding should be a minimum of 0.25 mm (10 mil) larger in each direction than the chip and 0.5 mm (20 mil) if a wire bond is to be included on the pad.
7. Chip and die bonding pads should be kept at least 2 mm (80 mil) away from the edges of the substrate.
8. Direct bonds are not to be made between chips, an intermediate bonding pad must be used.
9. Wire lengths for die bonds must be minimal, with a maximum of 2.5 mm (100 mil). Wire bonds must never cross.
10. Die bonding pads should be a minimum of 0.5 mm (20 mil) square and placed as near as possible to the minimum 0.4 mm (16 mil) from the chip bonding pad and its relevant bond on the die.
11. All lines for components must be parallel to the two major axes of the substrate (Manhattan geometry). Resistor outlines should preferably be rectangular or top hat (Figure 7.7(b)).
12. The normal spacing between resistors and the substrate edge should be at least 0.7 mm (30 mil).
13. Resistor dimensions should be greater than 1 mm (40 mil) and preferably as large as possible. Matched resistors should be identical in shape and placed side by side, pointing in the same direction in relation to the squeegee.
14. Ends of the resistors must overlap conductors by a minimum of 0.4 mm (16 mil) all around.
15. Unless the trimmer to be used has intelligence, a resistor loop cannot be tested and trimmed. The conductor path must be broken and later joined by a wire bond, soldering or using silver-loaded epoxy (see Figure 7.7(b)).
16. Capacitors should be no closer to the edge of a substrate than 0.5 mm (20 mil).
17. The top conducting plate of a capacitor should be 0.25 mm (10 mil) smaller in each direction than the dielectric. The dielectric can be either 0.4 mm (10 mil) larger or smaller in each direction than the lower conducting plate.
18. Alignment marks for layers should be located within the substrate borders. Preferably there should be two sets on diagonally opposite sides of the substrate. One method employs a square within a square matrix with

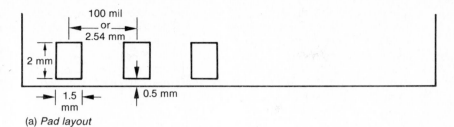

(a) *Pad layout*

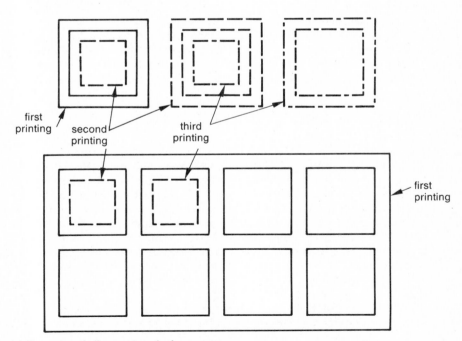

(b) *Manhattan geometry; no closed resistor loops*

(c) *Examples of alignment marks for screens*

Figure 7.7   Layout rule diagrams

subsequent layers filling one of the squares. (Note there is a considerable difference between the two examples given in Figure 7.6(c). In the first all subsequent alignments are relative to the previous one. With the second they are all relative to the first layer printed.)

19. Resistor dissipation should be kept to less than the paste manufacturer's recommended value, normally 40 mW/mm^2 (see Chapter 8, section 8.2).
20. Typical small outline semiconductor packages and some chip capacitor outlines are shown in Figures 7.8 and 7.9.
21. Where computer-aided design methods are used to lay out the design, the following colors are suggested for the various layers:

Conductor layer 1	Red
Conductor layer 2	Blue
Resistors	Black (with appropriate shading or paste numbering)
Crossovers	Brown
Dielectrics	Yellow
Glaze	Green
Solder	Orange

Once the artwork for the circuit is completed, the layout is transferred through the photographic process, previously discussed, to the screens. Product cost reduction and increased throughput can be achieved if several circuits are printed simultaneously. In transferring the artwork to a screen it is passed through a step-and-repeat process so that the pattern on the screen is for multiple circuits. Figure 7.10 shows two examples where 6 and 25 circuits are printed simultaneously on prescribed substrates.

7.7   Computer aided design (CAD)

The use of computer aided design can considerably simplify and speed up the design and layout of a thick-film circuit (Fu and Yang, 1985; Kos, 1985). There is today a growing range of software that can run on personal computers, allowing inexpensive CAD workstations. Analog and digital simulation as well as schematic diagram layouts are often part of printed circuit board software and they can be adopted for thick-film work. The remaining task is the actual layout of the circuit. While thick-film programs can be purchased commercially, it is a relatively simple task to write in extended BASIC or turbo PASCAL a layout program, including such functions as computing component sizes given input parameters such as value, dissipation and paste characteristics. While placement of the component is done manually, design rule checking can be built in. With most personal computers, at least eight colors and hence eight layers are possible. The color scheme given in the previous section is suggested provided one interchanges white for black on screen.

The commercial packages (HP, 1987) may include component placement and automatic routing, giving due regard to component dissipation and value. Even

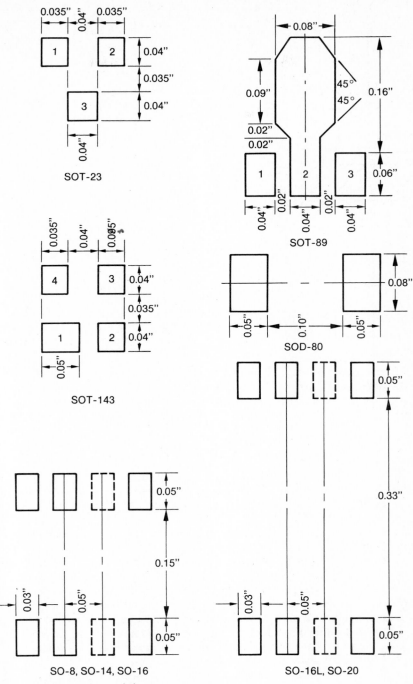

Figure 7.8 Small outline pad sizes

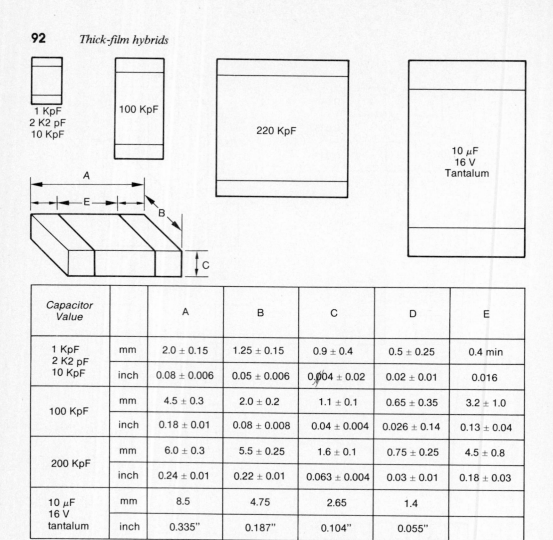

Capacitor Value		A	B	C	D	E
1 KpF 2 K2 pF 10 KpF	mm	2.0 ± 0.15	1.25 ± 0.15	0.9 ± 0.4	0.5 ± 0.25	0.4 min
	inch	0.08 ± 0.006	0.05 ± 0.006	0.004 ± 0.02	0.02 ± 0.01	0.016
100 KpF	mm	4.5 ± 0.3	2.0 ± 0.2	1.1 ± 0.1	0.65 ± 0.35	3.2 ± 1.0
	inch	0.18 ± 0.01	0.08 ± 0.008	0.04 ± 0.004	0.026 ± 0.14	0.13 ± 0.04
200 KpF	mm	6.0 ± 0.3	5.5 ± 0.25	1.6 ± 0.1	0.75 ± 0.25	4.5 ± 0.8
	inch	0.24 ± 0.01	0.22 ± 0.01	0.063 ± 0.004	0.03 ± 0.01	0.18 ± 0.03
10 μF 16 V tantalum	mm	8.5	4.75	2.65	1.4	
	inch	0.335"	0.187"	0.104"	0.055"	

Figure 7.9 Dimensions of selected chip capacitors

VLSI CAD geometric layout software can be employed for manual layout of a thick-film circuit.

The difficulty with most CAD systems is that the output for each layer must be converted into a photographic negative so that a screen can be made. To do this, a photoplotter is required and these are considerably more expensive than the personal computer CAD workstation. Fortunately the precision required for thick-film microelectronics is considerably less than that needed for integrated circuits and simple photoplotters can be made by adapting digital *xy* plotters. The color pens are replaced by holders of various apertures, each containing a green LED turned on and off by the pen up/down control signal. Green LEDs are used to give the best match to the film's spectral response. The LEDs are frequently in direct contact with the film.

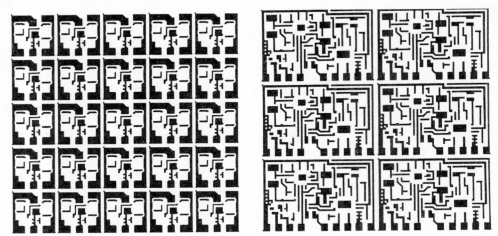

Figure 7.10 Multiple circuit printing onto prescribed substrates which reduces product cost and increases throughput

Source: With permission from Philips Australia.

If no photoplotter is available, then the output from the CAD system can be plotted at ×10 size and used as a master artwork to prepare manually taped layouts on polyester sheets or cut Rubylith sheets. A standard photographic reduction step produces the photographic film for screen preparation. Although it is still a part manual process, the use of CAD still speeds up the design and layout stages.

Figure 7.11 shows a workstation in use, while Figures 7.12 and 7.13 show the circuit schematic and final layout.

Figure 7.11 Designer using a computer aided design workstation to lay out a thick-film circuit

Source: With permission from Plessey Australia.

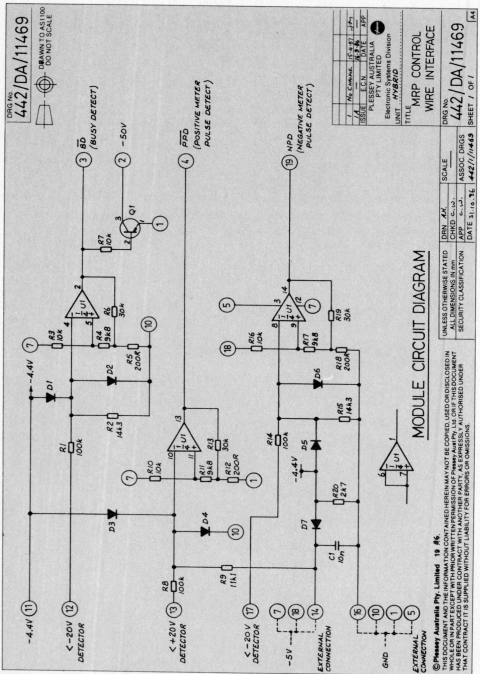

Figure 7.12 Schematic diagram of a module

Source: With permission from Plessey Australia

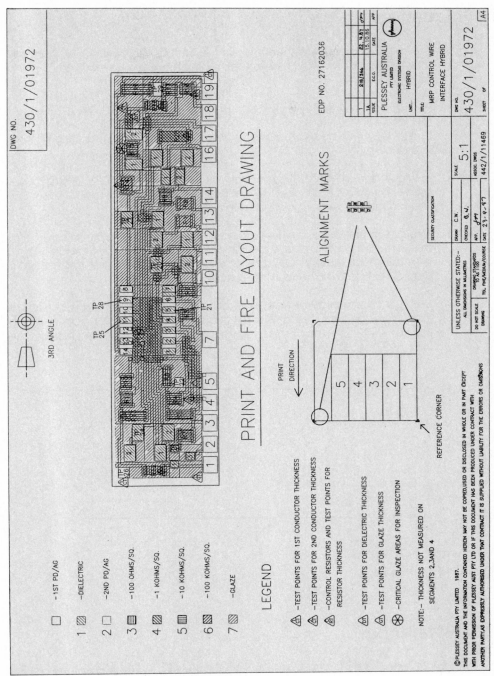

Figure 7.13 Layout of module given in Figure 7.12

Source: With permission from Plessey Australia

7.8 Exercises

1. Assuming resistor paste sheet resistances of 100, 1000 and 10 000 ohm per square, what paste would you select to print the following resistors?
   (a) 3300 ohm
   (b) 2000 ohm
   (c) 500 ohm
   (d) 1500 ohm
   In making your decision, consider the factors of cost and final printing tolerance.

2. A circuit consists of four resistors of values 15, 25, 8 and 75 kohm. To cut production costs it is hoped to print all the resistors with the 10 kohm per square paste. How do you suggest this can be done?

3. A thick film unit produces resistors with a tolerance before trimming of ±25 percent. If a resistor has to be trimmed to 1000 ohm ±1 percent and is to be made using 1000 ohm per square paste, what aspect ratio would you design the resistor to have?

4. Using a graph and the decade range of sheet resistance pastes of Exercise 1, design the layout for the simple attenuator pad given in Figure 7.14. The input and output are to be on one side of the 25 × 12 mm substrate.

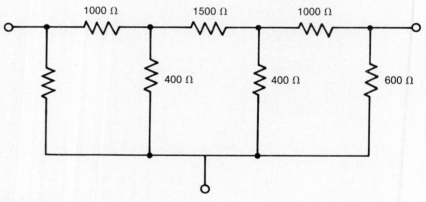

Figure 7.14 Exercise 4

7.9 References

Chen, T. M. and J. G. Cottle (1986), 'Physical Model of Burst Noise in Thick-Film Resistors', *Solid State Electronics*, vol. 29, no. 9, pp. 865–72.

Fu, S. L. and C. C. Yang (1985), 'A Computer Aided Layout System for Multilayered Hybrid Circuits', *Proc. 1985 International Symposium on Microelectronics*, 11–14 November, Anaheim, Cal., pp. 118–22.

Gosselin, J. P., F. J. Anders and R. M. Rosenberg (1975), *New Low Temperature Coefficient of Resistance Thick Film Resistors for Potentiometers*, Du Pont Electronic Materials Division, Wilmington, De.

HP (1987), 'HP Engineering Graphics System Hybrid Circuit Design Module', *Technical Data*, February, Hewlett-Packard Co., Palo Alto, Cal.

Janoska, I. (1983), *Thick Film Sensors*, SA Institute of Technology, Microelectronics Centre, Adelaide, South Australia, Report YA-14.

Kos, A. (1985) 'Computer-Aided Topology Design with Minimization of Thermal Interactions', *Proc. 1985 International Symposium on Microelectronics*, 11–14 November, Anaheim, Cal., pp. 123–6.

Mathews, R. K. (1973), *Thick Film Microcircuits*, SA Institute of Technology, Microelectronics Centre, Adelaide, South Australia, Report OR 22.

Microelectronics Centre, SA Institute of Technology Student Experiments, SA Institute of Technology, Adelaide, South Australia, various.

Milson, P. J. (1973), *Thick Film Microcircuits*, SA Institute of Technology, Microelectronics Centre, Adelaide, South Australia, Report OR 23.

Pitt, K. E. and R. J. Gledhill (1984), (author's discussions with), Middlesex Polytechnic, London.

Ringo, J. A., E. H. Stevens and D. A. Gilbert (1976), 'On the Interpretation of Noise in Thick Film Resistors', *IEEE Trans*, vol. PHP-12, no. 4, pp. 378–80.

Sinnadurai, F. N., P. E. Spencer and K. J. Wilson (1980), 'Some Observations on the Accelerated Aging of Thick Film Resistors', *Electrocomponent Science and Technology*, vol. 6, pp. 241–6.

8 Additional circuit design concepts

8.1 Introduction

Conceptually, the design of low frequency lumped thick-film circuits is relatively straightforward and is simply an extension of discrete circuit design. The two-dimensional layout of the design must be undertaken in accordance to the process layout rules (Chapter 7 and Appendix B). Unfortunately, with all engineering, at the extremities there are increasing difficulties. This is the case with thick film if the power levels or frequency of operation becomes increasingly high. In this chapter, the simple design approach will be illustrated, followed by an examination of some of the more difficult problems that can arise.

8.2 Low-frequency circuit design

The majority, if not all, of the low frequency circuits require the calculation of resistor areas, the placement of chip components (capacitors and semiconductors) and appropriate conductor routing to interconnect the circuit. Consider the pulse width modulator given in Figure 8.1. The calculations for the resistors are illustrated using R_1. It must have the correct aspect ratio to achieve the required absolute value and be of sufficient area to dissipate all power. Selecting a 10 000 ohm per square paste, the typical dissipation allowed is 40 mW per square mm, although values of up to twice this amount are possible. The power dissipated in R_1 is the root mean voltage across it divided by its value:

$$P_{R_1} = \frac{10^2}{15\,000}$$
$$= 6.7 \text{ mW}$$

The aspect ratio (length l, width w) must be:

$$10\,000\,\frac{L}{W} = 15\,000$$

$$\text{or} \qquad \frac{L}{W} = 1.5 \qquad\qquad (8.1)$$

To satisfy the power dissipation requirements:

$$L \cdot W \geqslant \frac{6.7}{1000} \quad \frac{1}{25 \; 40}$$
$$= 0.1675 \text{ mm}^2 \tag{8.2}$$

Solving these two equations gives the minimum dimensions for R_1, namely $L = 0.168$ mm and $W = 0.112$ mm. Since the preferred smallest dimension for a resistor is 1 mm, then the component size must be scaled accordingly, giving $L = 1.5$ mm and $W = 1$ mm.

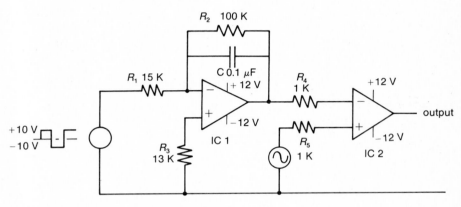

Figure 8.1 Pulse width modulator

These calculations have assumed the resistor is to be left untrimmed, that is, the printed value with associated tolerance is adequate. The printed tolerance can vary considerably depending upon the skill of the operator and size of run. It can vary from ±15 to ±25 percent (Figure 8.2(a)). If this is too large a spread then the resistor must be designed so that it can be trimmed to its correct value with a final tolerance of ±1 percent. Incidentally, there is little point in trimming resistors to a tolerance worse than the normal 1 percent as there are no economic gains. Some manufacturers adopt a policy of trimming all resistors.

Because a resistor can only be trimmed up in value, the resistor must be designed to have a mean value less than its desired value by at least the tolerance of printing. Using the extremity given above, that is resistors printed to ±25 percent, R_1 is designed to have a value of 15 000 less 25 percent (theoretically 20 percent is all that is needed), or 11 250 ohm (Figure 8.2(b)). The calculations are repeated, resulting in $L = 1.125$ and $W = 1$ mm. The dimensions of the remaining resistors in the circuit are calculated in an identical fashion, choosing an appropriate paste type, deciding if a trim is necessary, calculating aspect ratio and then dissipation. In the majority of cases, resistors can all be the minimum size set by the process. Such is not the case for the regulator circuit shown in Figure 8.3. Here the current capacity of a three-terminal chip regulator is increased by adding a power transistor. A 2 ohm resistor R_3 is included in the collector circuit, not

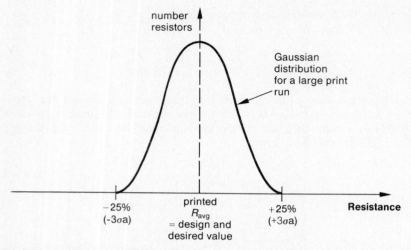

(a) *Correction to the resistor design value to ensure all printed resistors can be trimmed*

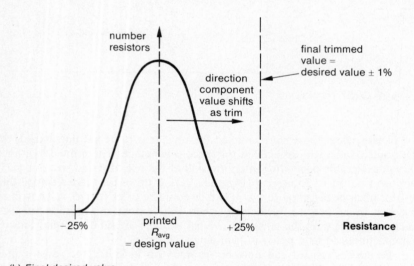

(b) *Final desired value*

Figure 8.2   Tolerance of an untrimmed printed resistor

only to reduce the transistor dissipation, but also to provide some protection against short circuits.

The power dissipated in R_3 under normal full load current conditions is 2 watt. Using the average dissipation figure, this would mean an area of 50 square mm. However, if a substrate area of this size were used there would be a failure, for the 40 mW per square mm working figure assumes that a normal circuit would have the majority of substrate area occupied by 'low dissipating' conductor lines.

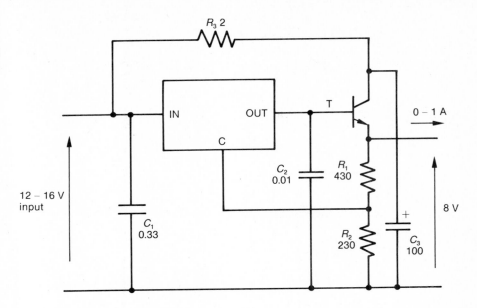

Figure 8.3 High current regulator

Note: All resistor values are in ohms and capacitors are in μF

Measurements reveal, for a resistor that covers a full 25 × 25 mm substrate, a 0.5 watt input power causes a temperature rise of 100°C. Consequently a 2 watt power load would cause such a thermal transient that the substrate could fracture. Thus, either an external resistor must be used or the substrate mounted on an adequate heat sink to remove the excess heat.

Non-standard rectangular resistors may also be required in other special circumstances, for example, large resistors that must fit into a restricted space or resistors that could need to be trimmed to over a wide range. An example of this is the gain of an operational amplifier that, depending upon the application, may have to be set to a value from 3–30. Figure 8.4 illustrates additional points that need to be considered. The first is the effect of a corner in a bent (*L* or meandering) resistor. Current crowds into the corner so that the corner square need only be considered as half a square in resistor calculation. To solve the problem of being able to trim a resistor over a width range, a top hat shape resistor is preferred. Again this is illustrated in Figure 8.4. The length is made to accommodate the range required. Note that when the trim cut is made as shown (dotted line) there are four corner squares each of approximately half a square (0.56).

Capacitors required for low-frequency circuits are large in value and therefore it is inefficient in area to print them. Chip capacitors are used. The limit in practical size to a printed capacitor is typically 100 pF. Some manufacturers avoid the problems of capacitor area requirements and poor electrical performance by adopting the policy to always use chip capacitors.

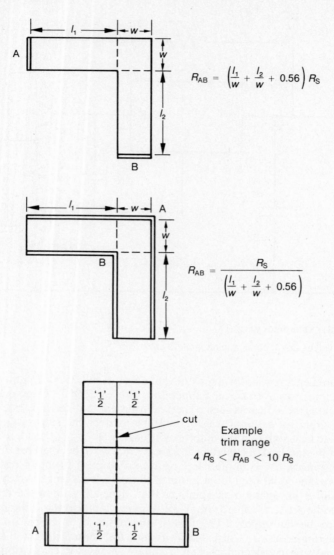

$$R_{AB} = \left(\frac{l_1}{w} + \frac{l_2}{w} + 0.56 \right) R_S$$

$$R_{AB} = \frac{R_S}{\left(\dfrac{l_1}{w} + \dfrac{l_2}{w} + 0.56 \right)}$$

Example
trim range
$4\,R_S < R_{AB} < 10\,R_S$

Figure 8.4 Non-rectangular resistor shapes including the top-hat resistor

8.3 Multilayer circuits

The advent of VLSI chips with large pin/pad out counts have highlighted the need
for multilayer circuits, consisting of alternate layers of conductors and insulators
with interconnection between conducting layers through vias. Using conventional
thick-film methods, the conducting layers under the insulator give rise to hillocks

(Figure 8.5(a)) so that the resulting surface for the following printings is very uneven. It is often referred to as the 'ploughed field' effect, and eventually limits the maximum number of layers that can be printed. An alternative approach is to employ a complementary printing where the complement of each conductor pattern is printed in low dielectric insulating paste, to fill the interspaces and restore the flat surface for subsequent printings. This process requires a clearance of 25–40 microns (1–1.5 mil) around conductors by the complementary dielectric and therefore accurate screen manufacture and printing alignment are required (Figure 8.5(b)). A modified complementary process is to make use of low temperature polyester pastes for the upper conducting and insulating layers. All soldering pads must be printed as part of the initial high temperature conducting paste.

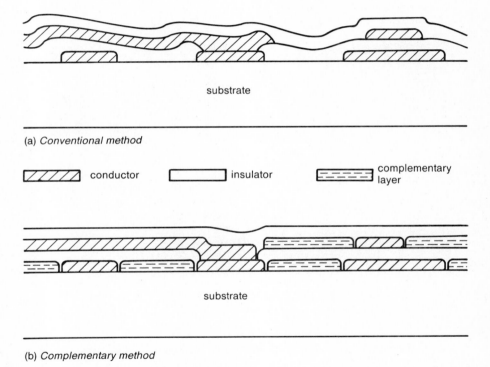

substrate

(a) *Conventional method*

| ▨ | conductor | ☐ | insulator | ☰ | complementary layer |

substrate

(b) *Complementary method*

Figure 8.5   Multi-layer circuits

Because of the interaction between resistor pastes and some dielectrics, it is often usual for all resistors to be printed early in the multilayer process so that they are printed directly onto the substrate. This gives improved printing tolerances and allows the substrate to remove any heat. Resistors to be trimmed must either be positioned so that there is no conductor pastes on top of them or printed on the upper surface.

8.4   High-frequency circuits

Invariably as the operating frequency is increased, inductors need to be introduced into the circuits. Such inductors can be added in chip form or printed using conductor pastes. Figure 8.6 shows several thick-film products with printed inductors. Many articles have been written deriving equations and empirical relationships for flat spiral inductors, both of circular and rectangular forms (Wheeler, 1928; Grover 1946; Bryan, 1955; Green, 1972). The majority of these are for printed wiring board construction. Figure 8.7 gives inductance values for square spiral inductors of turns 2–10 where the inner dimensions can be 3, 5 or 7 mm square. The quality factor of the inductors (Q) depends on many considerations and particularly the paste type used in the printing. Gold pastes will give Qs of a factor 3–10 higher than silver-palladium pastes. The latter case can be improved by coating the silver-palladium conductor tracks with a flux and then dip soldering. Improvements of a factor of 5 are typical.

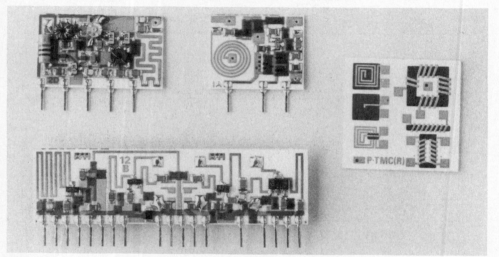

Figure 8.6   Examples of circuits using printed thick-film inductors
Note: The far right unit employs a ferrite paste.
Source: With permission from Philips Australia.

Another factor of importance is the method of connection to the inner portion of the inductor. Three possibilities exist: a wire bond, a soldered wire link of large diameter, or a dielectric crossover. The inductor value must take into consideration this extra length. If silver-palladium is used, then there is very little difference between all three methods at RF to VHF frequencies. Should a gold conductor be used, then the soldered wire gives the best results. (Printing the inner solder pad with a platinum-gold paste gives improved reliability.) Figure 8.8 presents results of Q measurements for a number of cases (Teng, 1986).

In addition to making inductors small, transformers are also possible (Casse, 1969). Two types are available: in one the two spirals are interwoven and printed at the same time side by side; whereas with the other, they are printed on top of

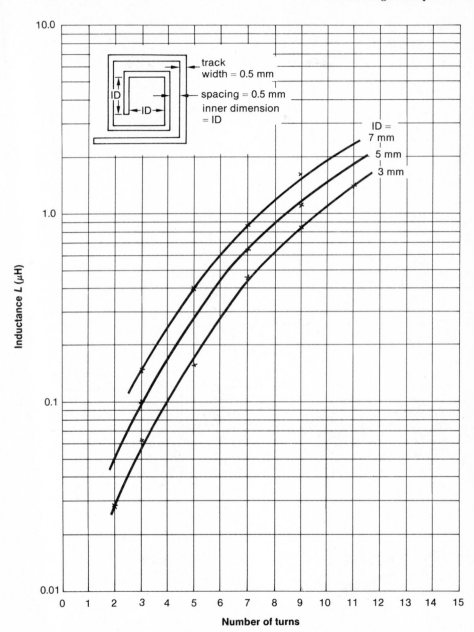

Figure 8.7 Inductance values and shape of printed flat spiral inductors

each other either with a dielectric layer separating them or they are placed on opposite sides of the substrate. Coupling coefficients of between 0.25 and 0.75 are reported.

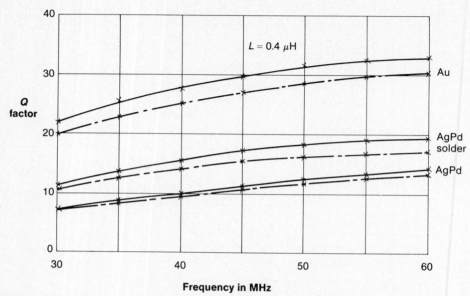

Figure 8.8 Plot of Q factor versus frequency for several inductor types. Heavy
line is a wire connection to inner contact. Dotted line a printed
conductor on a crossover dielectric

Ferrite pastes are available to improve the permeability and therefore increase
the value of inductance per area of substrate occupied. Printed toroids are possible
as well as distributed LC delay lines. The correct ferrite paste must be selected for
the frequencies in use and care must be taken to ensure that the ferrite paste is
compatible with the conductor paste used. Should this not be the case, then the
ferrite paste significantly lowers the Q and often the inductance value.

In addition to using inductors at high frequencies the thick-film process has
inherent within it the ability to make distributed RC networks (Matthews, 1975;
Pitt, 1978; Bose, 1974) and these can sometimes be employed to replace inductors.
They have applications in the area of low and high pass filters as well as band pass
and band stop types. Figure 8.9 provides several illustrations.

8.5   Thick film at microwave frequencies

Thick-film techniques can be applied at microwave frequencies up to 10 GHz (X
band). Two approaches are used: lumped element and distributed network
(Caulton and Sobol, 1970). Figure 8.10 shows a 460 MHz oscillator using
microstrip techniques. No matter which is used the resultant performance is
severely affected by the properties of the pastes and substrates selected as well as
the edge definition of the printed lines. We will now consider these methods.

The lumped circuit approach means that the components used have
inductance and capacitance values that do not change with frequency. Consider

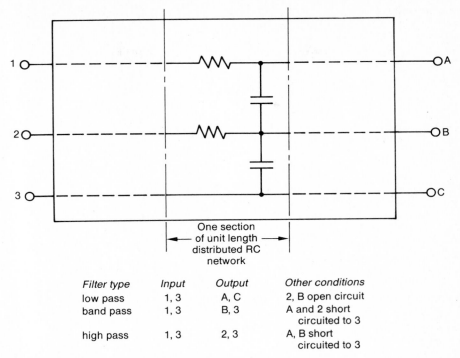

Filter type	Input	Output	Other conditions
low pass	1, 3	A, C	2, B open circuit
band pass	1, 3	B, 3	A and 2 short circuited to 3
high pass	1, 3	2, 3	A, B short circuited to 3

Figure 8.9 Examples of thick-film distributed networks

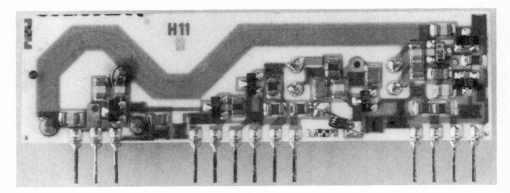

Figure 8.10 A 460 MHz voltage controlled oscillator using micro strip techniques to form the resonators

Note: The stripline had to be bent to fit into the available substrate size.

Source: With permission from Philips Australia.

the section of transverse electric magnetic (TEM) transmission line as shown in Figure 8.11. The line has distributed series resistance and inductance and shunt distributed conductance and capacitance. If this line is terminated in a load impedance Z_L, then the input impedance to line is given by (Caulton and Sobol, 1970):

$$Z_{IN} = Z_O \left\{ \frac{Z_L \cosh \gamma l + Z_O \sinh \gamma l}{Z_O \cosh \gamma l + Z_L \sinh \gamma l} \right\} \tag{8.3}$$

where Z_O is the characteristic impedance of the line and is given by:

$$Z_O = \sqrt{\frac{r + j\omega L}{g + j\omega C}} \tag{8.4}$$

and γ is the propagation constant:

$$\gamma = \sqrt{(r + j\omega L)(g + j\omega C)} \tag{8.5}$$

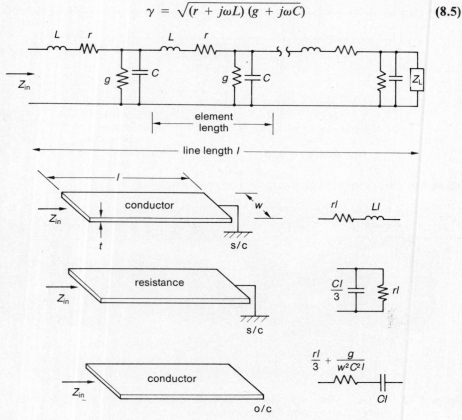

Figure 8.11   Distributed transmission line and resultant lumped components

For a short length of transmission line ($<\lambda$, where λ is the wavelength) short circuited at the load end ($Z_L = 0$), the input impedance is inductive, that is:

$$Z_{IN} \approx rl + j\omega Ll \tag{8.6}$$

and the quality factor of the resulting inductor:

$$Q = \omega \frac{L}{r} \tag{8.7}$$

It can also be shown that the inductance in nanohenries of a straight rectangular strip of conductor of length l, width w and thickness t (all in mm) is given by:

$$L = 0.20 \left(ln \frac{l}{w + t} + 1.19 + 0.22 \frac{(w + t)}{l} \right) \tag{8.8}$$

Should the transmission line be made of a resistor paste, then, by neglecting the series inductance and shunt conductance terms (small compared to r and C) then:

$$Z_{IN} \approx \frac{rl}{1 + \dfrac{j\omega Cl + rl}{3}} \tag{8.9}$$

The element not only has a resistance $r.l = R_s(l/w)$ (where R_s is the paste sheet resistance), but it also has a shunt capacitor $C.\frac{1}{3}$ or one-third of the total distributed capacitor of the line. If we return to a low resistance conductor paste line of short length and now open circuit the end (Z_L = infinity), then the input impedance is now capacitive.

$$Z_L \approx \frac{rl}{3} + \frac{g}{\omega^2 C^2 l} - \frac{1}{j\omega Cl} \tag{8.10}$$

Again there is a $\frac{1}{3}$ term, this time a series resistance due to the resistance of the paste. Thus the first resistance term is:

$$\frac{rl}{3} = \frac{R_s}{3} \frac{l}{w} \tag{8.11}$$

where R_s is the paste sheet resistance. The second resistance term is due to the dielectric loss and may be written as:

$$\frac{g}{\omega^2 C^2 l} = \frac{\tan \gamma}{\omega Cl} \tag{8.12}$$

where $\tan \gamma$ is the loss factor.

Using these open-circuited and short-circuited lines (Figure 8.11) resistance, capacitance and inductive elements can be formed. These can be grouped together to form 'lumped' microwave circuits.

The distributed network approach is to employ quasi TEM transmission lines. Three approaches have been used as shown in Figure 8.12. The most common is the microstrip line consisting of a conducting strip transmission line above a conducting ground plane. Both sides of the substrate are employed. The remaining two schemes are duals. They use only one side of the substrate and allow easy shunt mounting of chip devices. The propagation is not TEM and is such that magnetic fields lie on the surface of the substrate allowing magnetic material to be placed on the substrate surface.

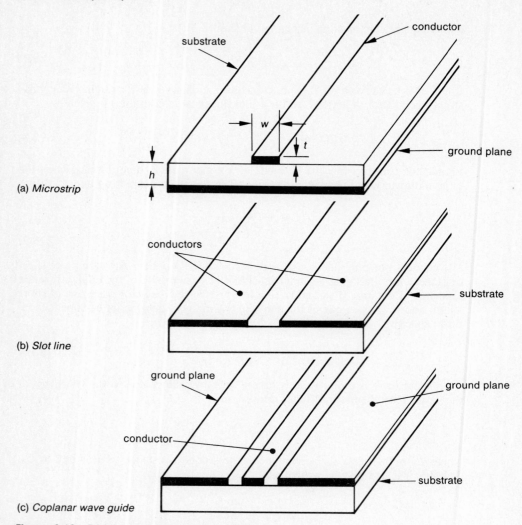

Figure 8.12   Distributed network approaches

Considering the microstrip transmission-line approach, Wheeler (1965) has shown a number of interesting properties (Figure 8.13). First, the properties are defined by the width (w) to height (h) characteristics, the height being the substrate thickness. Thus the line characteristic impedance is controlled by the width w and for a 50 ohm impedance w/h is approximately unity. Also of interest is the wavelength in the transmission line which changes little with the width (or Z_0) while the attenuation increases with substrate thickness and decreases with track width. The TEM mode of propagation is assumed, that is:

$$\frac{h\sqrt{\epsilon}}{\lambda} \ll 1 \tag{8.13}$$

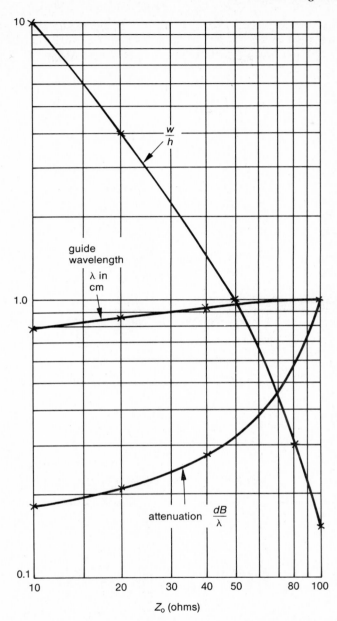

Figure 8.13 Characteristics of microstrip line showing attenuation, line wavelength and required dimensions for a particular characteristic
impedance

where h is the substrate thickness of dielectric constant ϵ and λ the wavelength.
For loss less lines ($r = 0$, $g = \infty$) the characteristic impedance and velocity of

propagation are related to the inductance L and capacitance C per unit length (equations 8.4 and 8.5). Thus L and C often need to be determined. A simple relationship has been derived for alumina substrates (Akello, 1979):

$$L = 7.82 \cdot 10^{-3} \; Z_0 + 0.03 \; \text{nH/mm} \qquad (8.14)$$

for $20 \leqslant Z_0 \leqslant 110$ ohms and:

$$C = 88.9 \cdot 10^{-3} \left(\frac{w}{h}\right) + 0.08 \; \text{pF/mm} \qquad (8.15)$$

for $0.5 \leqslant \dfrac{w}{h} \leqslant 6$

From these it can be seen that lines of high impedance (w small) are inductive, while low-impedance lines are capacitive. Using lines of differing impedances, networks can be made as illustrated in Figure 8.14 (Edwards, 1981).

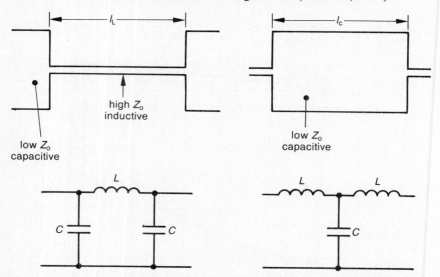

Figure 8.14   Simple filter networks built using microstrip line and their lumped equivalents

For a 50 ohm transmission line, the line width is equal to the thickness of the substrate, that is, 0.625 mm (25 mil). For inductive lines, the line width can be considerably less than the minimum 0.5 mm conductor width. Consequently, microstrip circuits are frequently manufactured on alumina substrates that are 1 mm (40 mil) thick.

Losses in a microstrip line occur for three reasons:

1. reflection;
2. dielectric loss; and
3. resistance loss.

Of these (1) is minimized by design while (2) and (3) through correct selection of materials.

The dielectric loss is:

$$\alpha_d = \frac{27.3 \sqrt{\epsilon} \tan \gamma}{\lambda} \tag{8.16}$$

where $\tan \gamma$ is the dielectric loss tangent.

For alumina substrates, typical values are $\epsilon = 9.7$, $\tan \gamma$ (95 percent alumina) $= 1.0 . 10^{-3}$ and $\tan \gamma$ (99 percent alumina) $= 0.2 . 10^{-3}$. The loss factor is very dependent upon the substrate surface finish. The conductor loss is:

$$\alpha_c = \frac{k \rho}{Z_0 \sqrt{\lambda}} \tag{8.17}$$

where ρ is the paste resistivity, Z_0 the line impedance and k the proportionality constant.

Various papers (Andersen and Olesen, 1972; Akroyd, 1974; Gitsham, 1974; Ramy et al., 1978; Holmes and Loasby, 1976) have presented measured results on paste and substrate types. In general, the lower the sheet resistance, the better the results. Gold pastes with reactive bonding or copper base metal pastes give Qs for resonant stubs or rings in excess of 350. Some designers choose to use a silver-palladium ground plane with the gold conductors as a means of reducing costs. The result is that Qs are reduced by a factor of 75 percent.

Thicker conductive layers tend to give a higher Q by at least a factor of 30 percent (Akello, 1979). Care must be taken at frequencies as low as 1 GHz as the paste thickness is only 3–4 skin depths, even with the gold pastes. If the roughness of the substrate surface is reduced or the percentage of alumina increased (even to 99.5 percent) then in some cases Qs can increase by up to a factor of 2 (Andersen and Olesen, 1972).

As stated earlier, the edge definition of the printed lines can severely affect performance. An alternative method of improving this is to employ an etching method to manufacture circuits. The total area of the substrate is screen-printed and then etched to form the circuit as is done with printed circuit boards. Potassium iodine/iodine etches are normally used for gold pastes and ammonia persulfate/mercury chloride used for copper pastes. Appendix C gives typical compositions of these etchants. Etched units give Qs that are typically 25–30 percent higher.

8.6 Thermal considerations

Where a circuit contains heat-sensitive elements and heat-generating components, it is critical that the layout takes these matters into consideration. Not only can offsets be generated, but very low oscillations can occur if the thermal feedback is positive. One way of mapping the isothermal lines is to simulate conditions using an analog simulation program such as SPICE (Haskard, 1983). Thermal resistance is analogous to electrical resistance as shown in Table 8.1.

Electrical flow	Thermal flow
$E = IR$	$T = P\theta$
where E is the potential difference (volts)	where T is the temperature difference (°C)
I the current (amps)	P the thermal power flow (watts)
R the electrical resistance	θ the thermal resistance (°C/watt)

Table 8.1 Analogy between electrical current and thermal heat flow

Using a grid approach to derive temperature gradients, the placement of components can be examined. Figure 8.15 shows the effect of changing position of a chip or resistor dissipating 2 watts on a 25 × 50 mm substrate.

DETERMINATION OF CHIP AND SUBSTRATE TEMPERATURES

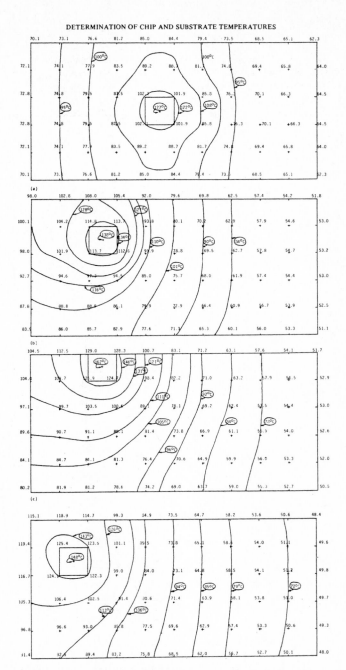

Figure 8.15 Isotherms for 25 × 50 mm substrates in still air with a resistor or chip dissipating 2 watts mounted at various positions

8.7   Exercises

1. A 50 ohm coaxial resistor termination as shown in Figure 8.16 is to be produced. The resistor is to be trimmed to 50 ohms ±1 percent by four equal cuts using a laser trimmer. Determine a method of how this can be achieved.

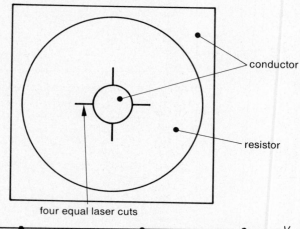

Figure 8.16   Exercise 1

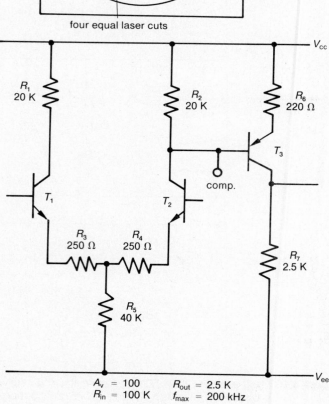

Figure 8.17   Exercise 2

$A_v = 100$ $R_{out} = 2.5$ K
$R_{in} = 100$ K $f_{max} = 200$ kHz

2. Figure 8.17 shows the circuit of a simple operational amplifier. For it to be an economically viable product, only three printings are allowed. Assuming decade resistor pastes 10 ohm to 1 Mohm are available, lay out the circuit. Using the transistor data given in Table 8.2, determine the amplifier gain, bandwidth, input and output impedance and any other parameter you consider important.

Parameter	BC547	BC557	Units
BF	225	180	
BR	2	1	
IS	$7.8 \cdot 10^{-14}$	$8.5 \cdot 10^{-14}$	A
RB	12	9	ohms
RC	0.01	1.2	ohms
RE	1.2	0.5	ohms
VA	80	80	volts
VB	—	—	
IK	—	—	
C_2	—	—	
NE	2	2	
IKR	—	—	
C_4	—	—	
NC	2	2	
TF	0.42	0.44	nsec
TR	0.5	0.46	nsec
CCS	0	0	
CJE	12.2	7.8	pF
PE	0.73	0.70	volts
ME	0.54	0.30	
CJC	6.3	11	pF
PC	1.0	1.0	volts
MC	0.31	0.31	

Table 8.2   SPICE data for BC547 and BC557 when used in non-saturation

3. Figure 8.18 shows a 40 MHz RF pre-amplifier. A 30 pF capacitor is to be used to resonate the tuned circuit. It is believed a printed inductor and 30 pF capacitor can be used. The transistors will be in small outline three-terminal packages and the dielectric paste has a dielectric constant of 20. Design the inductor and complete the layout.

8.8   References

Akello, R. J. (1979), 'Simple Formulae for Computing Microstrip Inductances and Capacitances', *Int. J. Electronics*, vol. 46, no. 3, pp. 225–8.

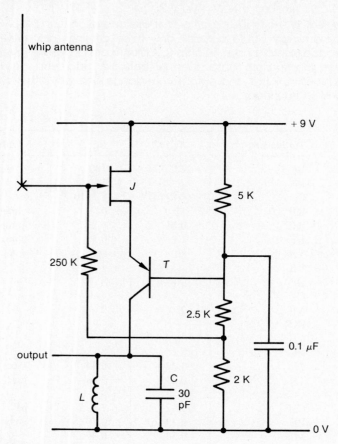

Figure 8.18 Exercise 3

Akroyd, R. J. (1974), *Microwave Applications of Thick Films*, SA Institute of Technology, Microelectronics Centre, Adelaide, South Australia, Report BL–18.

Andersen, E. and Olesen, S. T. (1972), *Thick-Film Microwave Circuits*, Danish Research Centre For Applied Electronics, Oslo, Horsholm.

Bose, N. K. (1974), 'Film Distributed Networks', *Microelectronics*, vol. 5, no. 3, pp. 30–7.

Bryan, H. E. (1955), 'Printed Inductors and Capacitors', *Tel-Tech*, vol. 14, no. 12, pp. 68–9, 120–2, 124.

Casse, J. L. (1969), 'Printed Transformers for High Frequency', *Electronic Engineering*, June, pp. 34–8.

Caulton, M. and H. Sobol (1970), 'Microwave Integrated-Circuit Technology—A Survey', *IEEE Journal Solid State Circuits*, vol. SC-5, no. 6, pp. 292–303.

Edwards, T. C. (1981), *Foundations for Microstrip Circuit Design*, Wiley Interscience Publication, Chichester, UK.

Gitsham, J. (1974), *Thick Film Microwave Circuits*, SA Institute of Technology, Microelectronics Centre, Adelaide, South Australia, Report BL–19.

Green, K. (1972), 'Design Curves for Flat Square Spiral Inductors', *Electronic Components*, 11 February, pp. 121–6.

Grover, F. W. (1946), *Inductance Calculations: Working Formulas and Tables*, Van Nostrand, New York.

Haskard, M. R. (1983), 'Determination of Chip and Substrate Temperatures', *Electrocomponent Science and Technology*, vol. 11, no. 1, pp. 35–42.

Holmes, P. J. and R. G. Loasby (1976), *Handbook of Thick Film Technology*, Electrochemical Publications, Ayre, Scotland.

Matthews, N. G. (1975), *Thick Film UHF Receiver Design*, SA Institute of Technology, Microelectronics Centre, Adelaide, South Australia, Report RE–26.

Pitt, K. E. G. (1978), 'Thick-Film Distributed Notch Filters,' *Microelectronics*, vol. 9, no. 1, pp. 18–21.

Ramy, J., M. Cotte, J. P. Bolloch, R. Schnitzler, J. Guena and C. Thebault (1978), 'Optimisation of the Thick and Thin Film Technologies for Microwave Circuits on Alumina and Fused Silica Substrates', *IEEE Trans Microwave Theory*, vol. MTT–26, no. 10, pp. 814–20.

Teng, Mui Tiang (1986), *Thick Film Inductor Measurements*, SA Institute of Technology, Microelectronics Centre Report.

Wheeler, H. A. (1965), 'Transmission-line Properties of Parallel Strips Separated by a Dielectric Sheet', *IEEE Trans Microwave Theory*, vol. MTT–13, pp. 172–85.

Wheeler, H. A. (1928), 'Simple Inductance Formulas for Radio Coils', *Proc. IRE*, vol. 16, no. 10, pp. 1398–400.

9 Thick-film sensors

9.1 Introduction

Thick-film sensors are growing rapidly in importance because of their simplicity, robustness and low cost. While special pastes are produced for some sensor types, many can be made using the standard pastes. This means that equipment, particularly belt furnaces, do not need to be adjusted to cope with the requirements set by the special pastes. Temperature, humidity, pressure and ionic concentration are examples of thick-film sensors. Table 9.1 summarizes some sensors that depend upon some property of the paste, while Figure 9.1 shows a number made at the Microelectronics Centre at the South Australian Institute of Technology.

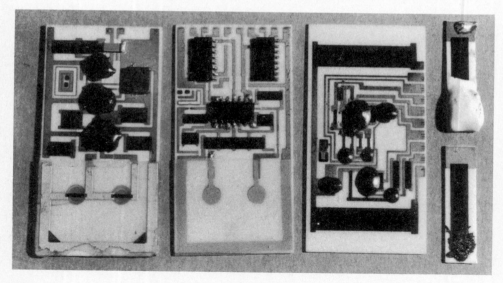

Figure 9.1 A selection of thick-film sensors. Left to right, piezo resistance and capacitance pressure sensors, constant temperature heating platform with temperature sensor and reference and ion selective electrodes.

Source: With permission from Microelectronics Centre South Australia Institute of Technology

Input	*Process*	*Sensor*	*Selected Reference*
Mechanical	Piezo resistance	Strain gauge Pressure transducer	Canoli et al. (1980) Dell' Acqua et al. (1981)
Thermal	Temperature coefficient	Resistor, conductor Resistor, dielectric	Gondek and Wojcicki (1983) Janoska and Haskard (1986)
Chemical	Nernst equation	Ion sensitive Reference electrode	Hoffman et al. (1984) Shoubridge et al (1985)

Table 9.1   Selected thick-film sensors

Still other sensors can be made using conventional circuit techniques. The most common is to print one plate of a capacitor, connecting it to the appropriate circuitry on the remainder of the substrate. The second plate of the capacitor is remote from the substrate and at an earthed potential. Differential capacitors may be used. Any movement of the remote plate will change the capacity and thus monitor the movement. Figure 9.2 illustrates the principle and shows how pressure, temperature, acceleration and displacement are measured in this way (Haskard, 1986). If an appropriate dielectric material is inserted between the two plates, then sensors such as humidity detectors can be produced (Gondek and Wojcicki, 1981).

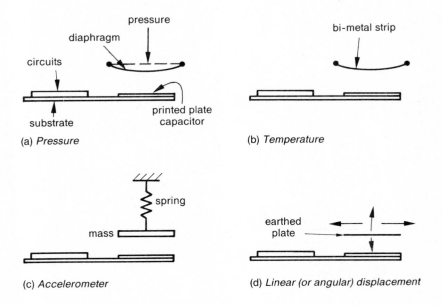

Figure 9.2   Examples of a capacitor sensor

The same principle applies to resistance. Sensors can be made using inter-digitized fingers of conducting paste over which is deposited a material, often a semiconductor like tin oxide, whose properties vary with some stimuli input, such as a particular gas (Graham et al., 1987). The material often works better at an elevated temperature so the fingers are printed on a dielectric layer under which a resistive heater, often a platinum-based paste for high temperature work, is printed. Figure 9.3 shows the basic construction. These sensors will not be discussed further as the range and type are only limited by the imagination.

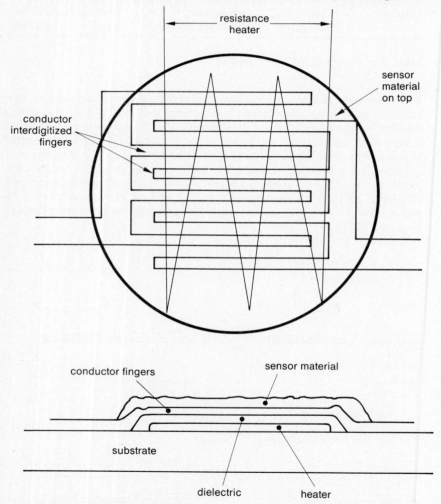

Figure 9.3   Simple resistive gas sensor

Returning to the paste types, we will first briefly consider the classes that employ special pastes and then those that use standard paste types.

9.2 Sensors based on special pastes

Paste manufacturers are constantly experimenting with new types suitable for sensors. Perhaps the most useful is the thermistor paste type. Figure 9.4 gives the characteristics of a typical paste. It comes with a sheet resistance of 10 kohm per square and has a negative temperature coefficient of -7000 ppm/$^\circ$C over the temperature range 25°–125°C. Peak firing temperature is 930°C which is considerably higher than the 800°C or 850°C required for the remainder of the pastes used (conductor, resistor, etc.) for a circuit.

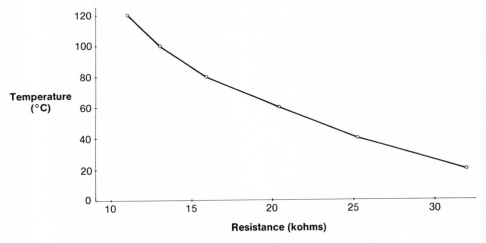

Figure 9.4 Characteristics of a thermistor paste

9.3 Sensors based on standard pastes

For the reasons already outlined, a considerable amount of effort has been put into fully exploiting the properties of standard pastes. The following are several examples.

9.3.1 Temperature sensors

Surprisingly, in the standard range of pastes, those with the highest temperature coefficients are the conductor pastes. Typical coefficients range from 1000–5000 ppm/$^\circ$C (Gondek and Wojcicki, 1981; Janoska and Haskard, 1983). An alternative method is to make use of resistor pastes printed on top of dielectric pastes (see section 7.5.1) (Janoska and Haskard, 1986; Rzasa and Potencki, 1986). Figure 9.5 shows how the resistance changes for various aspect ratios while Figure 9.6 compares the change in temperature coefficient (including sign) for a resistor of 4:1 aspect ratio printed on an alumina substrate and dielectric. A simple bridge consisting of two resistors on dielectric and two on the substrate connected to an operational amplifier makes a simple electronic thermometer (Figure 9.7) (Janoska and Haskard, 1985). The temperature range is 20° to 120°C with linearity typically ±3 percent. The circuit can be extended to become a constant

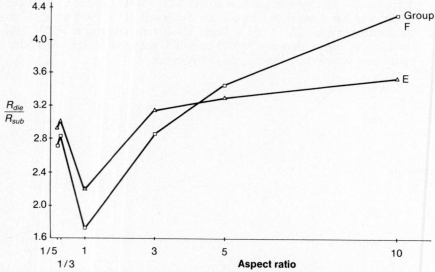

Figure 9.5 Ratio of resistance on a dielectric to resistance on a substrate versus aspect ratio for two paste combinations

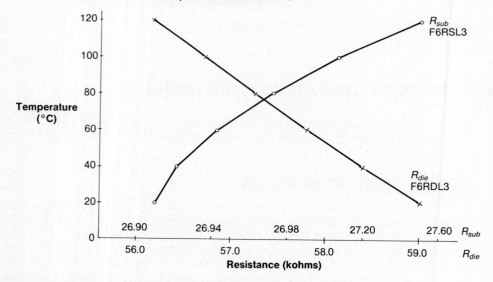

Figure 9.6 Typical resistance versus temperature for a resistor of 4:1 aspect ratio printed on an alumina substrate and on a dielectric paste

temperature platform as shown in Figure 9.8. Heaters are printed resistors and the circuit when produced on a 25×50 mm substrate can be used as a constant temperature probing station or a constant temperature platform for another circuit, such as a crystal oscillator, printed on the reverse side. When used as a probing station in still air conditions and from a cold start, the heating table oscillates about the required temperature for two cycles before settling down. The thermal settling time is typically 2 minutes. Maximum temperature is limited by the 5 watt heating resistors and in open, still air conditions is typically 80°C. In an insulated chamber, the maximum temperature is increased to 120°C, reaching the set temperature in about 30 seconds.

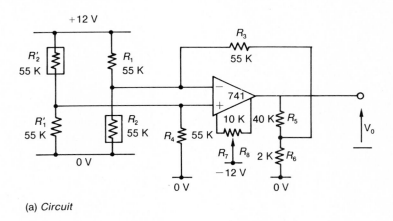

(a) *Circuit*

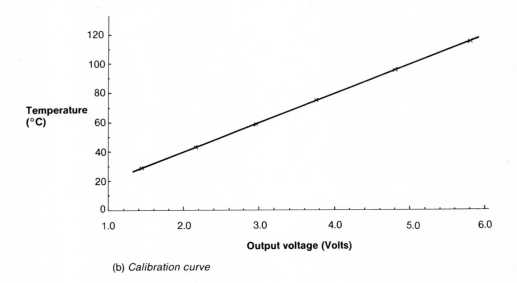

(b) *Calibration curve*

Figure 9.7 Electronic thermometer

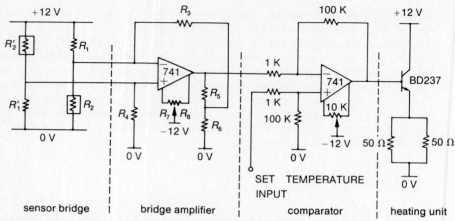

Figure 9.8 Constant temperature platform circuit diagram

A further method of measuring temperatures using standard pastes is to make a thermocouple or thermopile using two different conducting pastes. If the formed junctions are at different temperatures an emf is generated due to the Seeback effect. Because paste compositions are not readily available, the emf generated has to be determined experimentally. Table 9.2 summarizes those junctions found to provide the maximum emf (Esmailzadeh et al., 1987). Surprisingly resistor pastes give the best results. To thermally isolate the hot junction from the cold one, junctions can be printed on dielectric layers.

Paste combination	Average measured emf $\mu V/°C/junction\ pair$
Ag Pd ESL 9635 ESL 2812 (100 ohm/square)	18.9
Au Pd ESL 6835A ESL 2812 (100 ohm/square)	16.2
Ag Pd ESL 9635 ESL 2811 (10 ohm/square)	15.2
Au Pd ESL 6835A ESL 2811 (10 ohm/square)	13.3
Au Pd ESL 6835A Ag DP 6320	9.4
Ag Pd ESL 9635 Ag DP 6320	8.0

Table 9.2 Emfs produced from thermopiles made using different thick-film pastes

9.3.2 Piezo-resistance sensors

Thick-film pastes show piezo-resistance properties as discussed briefly in Chapter 7. Using this property, strain gauges, pressure transducers and other sensors can be manufactured. A difficulty with the high temperature pastes on alumina substrates is their restricted use through the high firing temperature. Pressure sensors have been made (Dell' Acqua et al., 1981), but to have adequate sensitivity the alumina diaphragms are large in diameter. A far easier family of pastes to use is the polymer paste family, for their low curing temperature allows them to be printed on most materials. Using a dielectric paste base, they can be screened directly on stainless steel diaphragms. Alternatively, plastic membranes (DiFiori and Haskard, 1986) such as polyester and polyimide can be employed. Figure 9.9 shows the results of such a paste printed on a 50 micron thick polyester diaphragm only 4 mm in diameter. Such circuits can have a large temperature coefficient and various bridge or sensor configurations need to be used to correct this. In spite of this, the concept is very useful and has even been applied to medical situations where, fortunately, the body temperature is almost constant, lessening the problems of temperature compensation. De Conno et al. (1986) describe a sensor, used to measure pressure in the stomach and intestines, being inserted on a conduit through the nose, while Beresnevicius and Haskard (1986) describe development of three interconnected pressure sensors, each 1 mm long and on a 1 mm spacing, to measure the pressure and direction in the sphincter of Oddi muscle.

9.3.3 Ion selective probes

The concentration of a particular ion in solution can be determined by measuring the difference in potential between an electrode, often sensitized to the particular ion by an electroactive material, and a reference electrode, such as a Ag/AgCl type, both inserted into the solution. The ionic concentration is related to the measured potential Δv by the Nernst equation:

$$\Delta v = \frac{2.303\,RT}{Z_i\,F}\log_{10}C_i$$

where:

C_i is the ionic concentration
R is the gas constant
T is the absolute temperature in $^\circ$K
Z_i is the charge of the ion of interest
F is Faraday's constant

A common application of this method is the measurement of pH (hydrogen power) using glass electrodes.

The ion selective probes can be readily fabricated using carbon polymer pastes (Hoffman et al., 1984) and, depending upon the electroactive sensitizing material, can respond to a whole range of ion types. Figure 9.10 shows typical

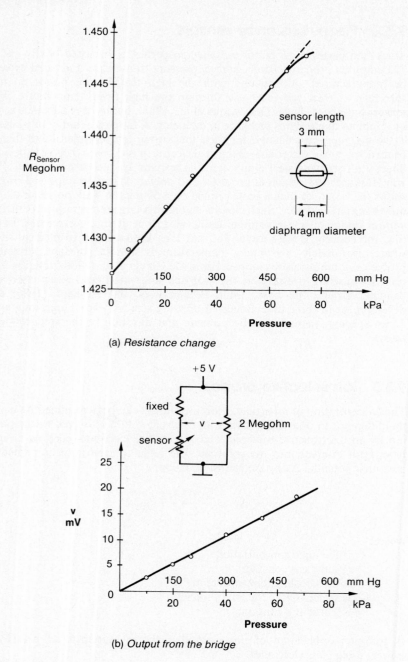

(a) *Resistance change*

(b) *Output from the bridge*

Figure 9.9 Simple pressure sensor employing polymer pastes on a polyester diaphragm

responses to pH, halogens and some heavy ions. The sensitizing material can be applied in powder form mixed with the polymer paste or vacuum deposited on top of the printed paste.

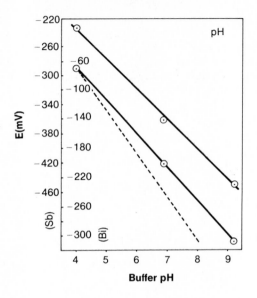

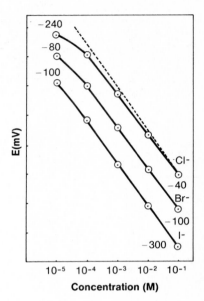

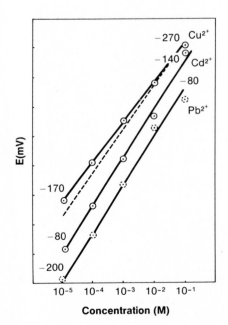

Figure 9.10 Various ion concentration measurements using sensitized carbon polymer paste electrodes. Dottled lines represent theoretical Nernstian responses

Reference electrodes can also be made using carbon polymer pastes (Shoubridge et al., 1985). Figure 9.11 shows the construction. The fact that both electrodes can be printed means that they can be miniaturized, and integrated with associated electronics. Bennier et al. (1986) describe the development of electrodes to measure the pH in the gut of humans, a pH typically in the range of 1–8. The electrodes were 1×2 mm in size and eight are to be mounted along a conduit and inserted into the gut through the nose.

A difficulty with all such electrodes is their high output impedance. Simple thick-film impedance transformation amplifiers (Mellor et al., 1982) buffer the electrodes and allow low-impedance metering circuits to be employed.

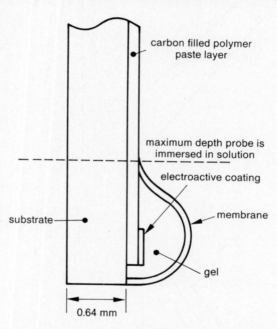

Figure 9.11 Construction of a reference electrode using thick-film carbon polymer pastes

9.4 Other related devices

There are many novel ideas how thick-film technology may be used for producing practical devices, some of which, although not strictly sensors, are related. Two will now be discussed.

9.4.1 Fast-acting thick-film fuses

Printed, thin conducting tracks could be used as fuses. However, there is a problem, namely the thermal inertia of the alumina substrate. Arising from the thermal sensor work previously discussed, it was proposed that the same method of printing the conductor fuse on top of a dielectric paste would provide thermal isolation and, therefore, speed up the 'blowing' of the fuse and reduce the let-through energy. Such is the case (Marriage and McIntosh, 1986). Comparisons with commercially available fuses indicate that the thick-film fuses let-through energy is some two orders less.

9.4.2 High-voltage isolation

In many areas, adequate high-voltage insulation is essential. Opto-isolators are one way of achieving this. An interesting property of the alumina substrates employed in thick-film technology is that they transmit infrared light. Consequently, it is possible to print the input circuit on one side of a substrate, the output circuit on the other and use the substrate to provide several kilovolts of isolation. Measurements and calculations show that when an infrared LED is used to trigger a light-triggered silicon-controlled rectifier (LASCR) through an alumina substrate of 0.625 mm (25 mil) thickness, the presence of the substrate requires only an increase in LED current of a factor of 2.5 to still reliably trigger the LASCR, yet the isolation voltage is increased by a factor of 14 (Silva and Haskard, 1983).

9.5 Exercises

1. The general purpose capacitor sensor discussed in the introduction is to be connected to an electronic circuit to provide: (a) an analog voltage output signal proportional to capacitance; and (b) a digital signal that is proportional to the capacitance. Suggest methods and circuits as to how you may do this.

2. List possible applications for the thermistor paste whose characteristics are given in section 9.2 and Figure 9.4.

3. Figure 9.12 shows the tangential and radial strain distribution of a clamped circular diaphragm. Determine the best shape and position for printing thick-film piezo-resistance sensors on the diagram.

9.6 References

Bennier, R., D. E. Mulcahy and M. R. Haskard (1986), *Combined Sensor for Measuring pH and Pressure in the Gut*, Microelectronics Centre, SA Institute of Technology, Adelaide, South Australia, Report RD–05.

Beresnevicius, R. and M. R. Haskard (1986), *Miniature Sensor to Measure Pressure in the Sphincter of Oddi*, Microelectronics Centre, SA Institute of Technology, Adelaide, South Australia, Report RD–06.

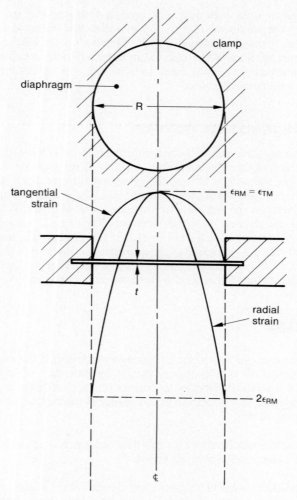

Figure 9.12   Exercise 3

Canoli, C., D. Malavasi, B. Morton, M. Prudenziata and A. Taroni (1989), 'Piezo-resistive Effects in Thick Film Resistors', *J. App. Physics*, vol. 51, pp. 3282–8.

de Conno, C., D. E. Mulcahy and M. R. Haskard (1986), *Combined Sensor for Measuring pH and Pressure in the Gut*, Microelectronics Centre, SA Institute of Technology, Adelaide, South Australia, Report RD–13.

Dell' Acqua, R., G. Dell' Orto and P. Vicini (1981), 'Thick Film Pressure Sensors: Performance and Practical Applications', *Third European Hybrid Microelectronics Conference*, Avignon, pp. 121–34.

DiFiori, A. and M. R. Haskard (1986), 'Thick Film Pressure Transducers', *Microelectronic Journal*, vol. 17, no. 1, pp. 35–41.

Esmailzadeh, R., D. E. Davey, M. R. Haskard and D. E. Mulcahy (1987), *Carbon Dioxide Alarm Module*, Microelectronics Centre, SA Institute of Technology, Adelaide, South Australia.

Gondek, J. J. M. A. and Wojcicki (1981), 'New Du Pont Composition Applied in Thick Film Temperature and Humidity Sensors', *Electrocomponent Science and Technology*, vol. 9, pp. 93–100.

Gondek, J. J. and M. A. Wojcicki (1983), 'New Thick Film Temperature Sensors Applied in Some Hybrid Measurement Devices', *Electrocomponent Science Tech.*, vol. 10, pp. 95–102.

Graham, M., M. R. Haskard and D. E. Mulcahy (1987), *Microelectronic Gas Detectors*, Microelectronics Centre, SA Institute of Technology, Adelaide, South Australia.

Haskard, M. R. (1986), 'General Purpose Intelligent Sensors', *Microelectronic Journal*, vol. 17, no. 5, pp. 9–14.

Hoffman, C., M. R. Haskard and D. E. Mulcahy (1984), 'Carbon Filled Polymer Paste Ion-Selective Probes', *Anal. Letters*, vol. 17, A13, pp. 1499–509.

Janoska, I. and M. R. Haskard (1983), *Thick Film Sensors*, Microelectronics Centre, SA Institute of Technology, Adelaide, South Australia, Report YG–14.

Janoska, I. and M. R. Haskard (1985), 'Thick Film Standard Paste Temperature Sensor Applications', *Sensors and Actuators*, vol. 8, pp. 3–9.

Janoska, I. and M. R. Haskard (1986), 'Thick Film Temperature Sensors Using Standard Pastes', *Active and Passive Electronic Components*, vol. 12, pp. 91–101.

Marriage, A. J. and B. McIntosh (1986), 'High-Speed, Thick Film Fuses', *Hybrid Circuits*, vol. 9, 1986, pp. 15–17.

Mellor, T. J., M. R. Haskard and D. E. Mulcahy (1982), 'A Teflon-Graphite Ion-Selective Probe with Integrated Electronics', *Analytical Letters*, vol. 15, A19, pp. 1549–55.

Rzasa, B. and J. Potencki (1986), 'Thick Film Resistors on Dielectrics as Temperature Detectors', *Active and Passive Electronic Components*, vol. 12, pp. 137–47.

Shoubridge, P., M. R. Haskard and D. E. Mulcahy (1985), 'Carbon Filled Polymer Paste Reference Electrodes', *Anal. Letters*, vol. 18, A12, pp. 1457–64.

Silva, R. and M. R. Haskard (1983), *Solid-State Relays*, Microelectronics Centre, SA Institute of Technology, Adelaide, South Australia, Report YG–15.

Appendix A

Screen care and preparation

The following description tells how screens are cleaned and prepared using the indirect method (polyblue material). The screens are stainless steel mesh stretched onto a cast then machined aluminium frame.

A.1 Screen pre-preparation

Screen mesh sizes of 165, 200 and 325 are normally used, 200 mesh being the preferred standard; 325 is used where fine work is required (microstrip or line widths less than 0.25 mm (10 mil)); 165 is used for screening solder pastes, or when large areas of conductor are required.

Screens must be clear of dust and grease. This will normally be so if the polyblue masks have been removed at the conclusion of printing, and screens stored properly.

Care must be taken at all times not to damage the screens, particularly with brushes.

Check the screen closely for any foreign matter caught in the mesh. Any polyblue can be removed by brushing with hypochlorite solution (e.g. household antiseptic bleach). Paste particles dried in the mesh are particularly difficult, and can only be removed by hard, but careful, scrubbing with clean water.

After using hypochlorite solution, the screen must be thoroughly rinsed in running deionized water, soaked in 2 percent acetic acid, and thoroughly rinsed again. The aluminium frame should also be scrubbed with the brush and acetic acid, to remove the 'caustic effloresence' that sometimes appears on aluminium.

The screen is stood up to dry naturally, if not to be used the same day.

A.2 Polyblue mask preparation

The indirect method of screen making will be described using the ULANO Bluepoly-2 film. It is sensitive to blue and near ultraviolet light. The size of material for various substrate sizes is given in Table A.1.

Substrate size	Polyblue size
12.5 × 25 mm ($\frac{1}{2}$ × 1 inch)	60 × 85 mm (2.5 × 3.75 inch)
25 × 25 mm (1 × 1 inch)	60 × 85 mm (2.5 × 3.75 inch)
25 × 50 mm (1 × 2 inch)	60 × 110 mm (2.5 × 4.5 inch)
50 × 50 mm (2 × 2 inch)	110 × 110 mm (4.5 × 4.5 inch)

Table A.1   Size of polyblue needed for various substrate sizes

Exposure to ultraviolet light is undertaken as follows. A piece of Rubylith, dull side up, is used as a non-reflecting base. First, place the polyblue film piece centrally in the exposure tray, emulsion (i.e. dull) side down. Next, the photo-negative (black for tracks and resistors) is placed emulsion-side down in the center of the polyblue film. (Look at the negative same way as tracks appear on substrate and turn over.) Any identification ciphers can be read facing emulsion side. Finally, lower the cover glass into place. It is important that the film and polyblue are sandwiched as shown in Figure A.1.

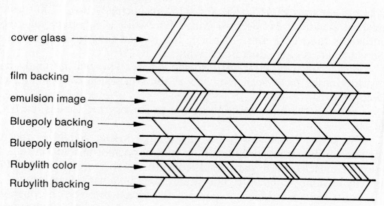

cover glass

film backing

emulsion image

Bluepoly backing

Bluepoly emulsion

Rubylith color

Rubylith backing

Figure A.1   Exposure of the polyblue

The exposure box should be switched on five minutes prior to use. An inbuilt timer can be used.

Push the exposure tray fully into the exposure box without hesitation. The amber light will indicate that timing has started. A buzzer and second amber light indicate the end of the exposure time.

The development solution consists of 400 ml of deionized water, plus 20 ml of hydrogen peroxide (100 vol). With freshly made developer, the development time will be typically 90 seconds.

Place the polyblue film in a developer dish emulsion side up using plastic tweezers and fully immerse immediately.

Wash the polyblue in running deionized water at 40°C until the pattern emerges and all the tracks are clear.

Rinse in cold deionized water.

Difficulties:

1. Under exposure —Polyblue is too soft; dissolves away in rinse or smudges when pressed into screen.
2. Over exposure —Polyblue too hard; will not adhere to screen.
3. Rinse or developer too hot —Polyblue wrinkles; too soft, smears when pressed into screen.
4. Developer too cold —Takes too long to develop, or will not rinse out.
5. Rinse too cold —Pattern will not clear.

A.3   Screen preparation

It is important that the pattern on the polyblue and hence the polyblue be mounted centrally on the screen. Most printer alignment facilities allow for some misalignment but this may be as little as ± 5 mm. This alignment can be done using a light box which has both a frame to hold the screen and marked positions on it indicating the various substrate sizes. These marks are used to position the exposed and developed polyblue.

The wet polyblue mask is placed emulsion side up on the light box and aligned in the target, or with the alignment pattern.

The screen should be soaking in the same water as the cold rinse, and while wet, placed over the polyblue mask, centrally in the frame and lightly clamped.

Using a roll of lint-free paper, absorb the water with gentle pressure, rolling and removing the wet paper. Too much pressure smudges the pattern, too little pressure and the mask will not adhere to the screen.

Remove the screen with the polyblue and allow it to dry for at least 6 hours (usually overnight).

When dried out, the Mylar backing is peeled off. Inspect the screen for blemishes.

A.4   Cleaning screens after printing

Re-use of screens and their masks is possible by immediately cleaning them after use. Remove excess pastes with a spatula and return to the paste jar.

The residual paste enmeshed in the screen can be removed by spraying the screen with methanol and scrubbing with a toothbrush. Use a stainless steel tray and remote light source so that the screen can be easily examined during cleaning, as shown in Figure A.2.

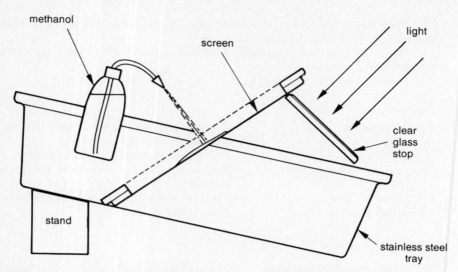

Figure A.2 Cleaning a screen after printing

Once the paste is all removed, wash the complete mask in methanol. Do not rinse in water, otherwise the mask will soften and distort. Stand the screen to dry, usually 5–10 minutes.

Should the mask not be required again, remove by brushing with hypochlorite solution as in section A.1.

Appendix B
Summary of thick-film layout rules

Artwork undertaken manually is generally done at $\times 10$ size using Manhattan geometry. There will be an artwork for each paste, including the masking or coating and solder pastes if used. Alignment marks should be included, preferably two sets on diagonal corners. This mark can be a series of solid squares within square outlines as illustrated in Figure B.1. Each layer has a smaller square that fits into a square on the previous layer and a larger square for alignment of the next layer.

While substrates can be obtained in almost any size by special order, most manufacturers of thick-film carry only a limited range. If need be, substrates can be cut or scribed and broken, but this adds to the product cost. It is best to check with manufacturers what stocks they carry or use one of the popular sizes. For example, 12.5×25 mm, 25×25 mm or 25×50 mm.

Resistor pastes generally come in decade ranges from 10 ohm to 1 Mohm per square. The dissipation allowed depends on the paste and substrate type. For the high temperature paste/alumina combination, 40 mW per square mm is typical. Figure B.1 provides information on conductor layout including external lead pads. In addition, the following rules should be adhered to:

1. Pads for semiconductor dice and chip components should be greater than 0.5 mm $\times$ 0.5 mm. In general, they should be the chip or die area plus 0.2 mm all round in each direction. Chip and bonding pads must be kept at least 2 mm from the substrate edge.
2. Bonding to semiconductor die. Direct bonds are not to be made between die. An intermediate pad is to be used. The wire lengths for bonds are to be no greater than 2.5 mm.
3. Resistors. The preferred aspect ratio is $\frac{1}{3}$–3 although $\frac{1}{5}$–5 can be used if a loss in printing accuracy can be tolerated. Resistors that are to be trimmed should be designed 25 percent lower than their final value. This is because resistors are trimmed up in value. If probing resistors, there needs to be a conductor area available at least 0.4×0.4 mm square. Figure B.1 gives other important dimensions for resistors.

139

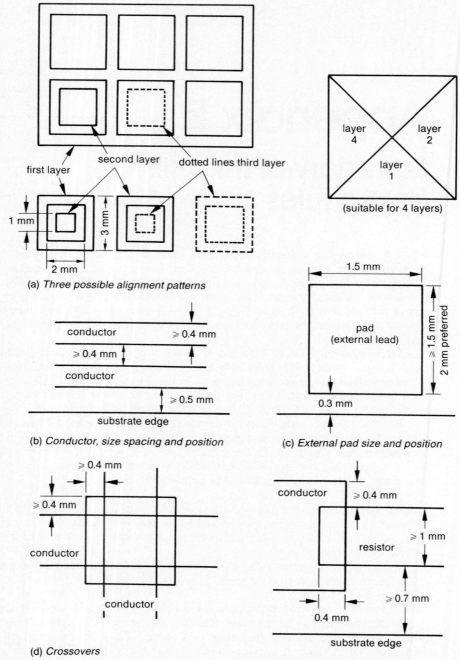

(a) *Three possible alignment patterns*

(suitable for 4 layers)

(b) *Conductor, size spacing and position*

(c) *External pad size and position*

(d) *Crossovers*

(e) *Resistor termination, size and position*

Figure B.1   Summary of thick-film layout rules

4. Dielectric pastes. The same minimum dimension rules apply as for a resistor. Additional rules are that crossover and other dielectric pastes over a conductor should surround the conductor by at least 0.4 mm. The distance for dielectric to an unrelated resistor to be at least 0.5 mm.

Appendix C
Etchant solutions for pastes

C.1 Gold pastes

Temperature 55°–60°C
50 g iodine
30 g potassium iodide
400 ml ethanol
50 ml DI water

C.2 Gold–palladium pastes

Temperature 20°–30°C
100 ml conc. nitric acid
100 ml conc. hydrochloric acid
200 ml DI water

C.3 Silver pastes

Temperature 35°–50°C
35 g ferric nitrate
40 ml DI water

C.4 Silver–palladium pastes

Temperature 35°–50°C
35 g ferric nitrate
40 ml DI water
10 ml conc. nitric acid

142

C.5   Copper pastes

Temperature 40°–50°C
240 g ammonium persulphate
1 ml mercuric chloride
1000 ml DI water

Index

Assemby
    chip, 57
    die bonding, 64
    epoxy, 60
    eutectic bonding, 60
    passive components, 60
    pick and place machines, 58
    soldered, 58
    surface mount technology, 9, 57, 60

Bonding (*see* Assembly)

Capacitors
    chip, 92, 101
    dielectric, 86
Cleaning process, 75
Clean rooms
    construction, 72
    contamination, 73
    general, 70
    house keeping, 74
    standards, 71
Computer aided design, 90
Conformal coating, 67
Constant temperature platform, 125

Design
    approach, 78
    CAD, 90
    distributed networks, 106
    inductors, 104
    layout rules, 87, Appendix B
    microstrip, 106
    microwave filter, 112
    minimum size components, 80
    print or chips, 83, 86
    resistors, 6, 82, 98, 100, 101
    thermal considerations, 101, 113
Distributed networks, 106, 109
Drying pastes, 45

Electronic thermometer, 124
Etched circuits, 113, Appendix C

Fillers, 21
Film thickness
    importance, 5, 28
    measurement, 28
    values, 24
Filters, 106, 112
Fine line techniques, 21
Furnaces
    atmosphere, 40, 46, 48
    chlorine effects, 46
    general, 45, 46
    infra red, 45, 49
    profile, 46, 48
Fuses, 130

High voltage, 85, 131

Inductors, 104
Inks (*see* Pastes)
Integrated circuits, 9

Layout rules, 87, Appendix B

Microelectronics
    classification, 1
    comparison technologies, 8, 10
Mircostrip, 106, 109
Multilayer circuits, 17, 102

Packaging
    casting, 67
    conformal coating, 67
    hermetic, 67, 68
    methods, 67
    moulded, 67
    TAB, 64
Pastes
    base metal, 31, 40
    binder, 34
    compositions, 32, 33, 34, 35, 39, 40
    conductor, 33, 34, 40, 41
    dielectric, 35, 40, 43
    firing temperature, 31, 36, 39, 40, 45, 46

fritted, fritless, mixed, 33, 34
mechanical bond, 33
reactive bond, 33
reactive pastes, 34
recrystallizing glass, 36
resistor, 34, 40, 42
resistor pigments, 34
rheology, 25
storage, 34
selection, 41
thermistor, 123
thermoplastic, 40
thermosetting, 40
types, 31, 106, 123
viscosity, 27
Pick and place, 58
Printed circuit board, 9
Printer
components, 15
operation, 27
printing methods, 22
snap off distance, 18, 22
substrate holder, 27

Resistors (*see also* Design)
aging, 85
noise, 85
on dielectrics, 86
piezo resistance, 85, 127
size calculations, 6, 80, 82
termperature coefficient, 83
voltage coefficient, 85

Safety, 70, 75
Screens
cleaning, 137
etched, 21
general, 15

mesh, 16
preparation, 19, Appendix A
selection, 80
Sensors
gas, 122
general, 120
ion selective, 127
piezo resistive, 127
pressure, 127
temperature, 123, 126
Settling time, 45
Sheet resistance, 5
Snap off distance, 18, 22
Squeegee, 15, 22
Step and repeat, 90
Substrates
compositions, 36
manufacture, 36, 38, 39
properties, 32, 39
surface, 24
thermal dissipation, 101
Surface mount technology, 9, 57, 60

Testing, 57, 68
Thermistor paste, 123
Thermopile, 126
Thick film
flow diagram, 7
history, 2
process overview, 3
Thin film, 2, 9
Trimming
abrasive, 49
laser, 50
passive and active, 7, 52, 57
tolerances, 49, 80, 83, 99
trim cuts, 52, 54

Writing machine, 28